# The Great Motorway Secret

By S. Addy

FCL Publishing
First Edition

Published by:
FCL Publishing
22 George Street
Maulden
Bedford
MK45 2DF

ISBN 0-9550899-0-5

First Published 2005

Printed by:
Newnorth
Newnorth House
College Street
Kempston
Bedford
MK42 8NA

# Foreword

The past twenty years have seen many changes in the way in which we do our shopping. The busy high street of old has been superseded by the large modern out-of-town 'sell everything' superstores.

When one of these superstores is sited near to a motorway junction, then for the motorist, it offers a real value-for-money alternative to a service station.

*The Great Motorway Secret* has identified nearly 100 of these well known superstores throughout England and Wales which are just minutes from a motorway junction. All the stores listed have toilet facilities, a café/restaurant offering great value meals*, a petrol station and of course everything else you'd expect from your local superstore.

Consult the guide before you start your journey, plan your stops, check the opening times and you should save pounds.

* Café / restaurant facilities may only be available at certain times, check with the store

# The Great Motorway Secret

## Contents

M1

**Leeds**

N

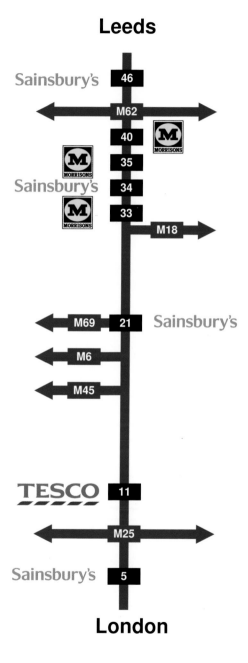

Sainsbury's 46

◄ M62 ►

40 MORRISONS

MORRISONS 35

Sainsbury's 34

MORRISONS 33

M18 ►

◄ M69 21 Sainsbury's

◄ M6

◄ M45

TESCO 11

◄ M25 ►

Sainsbury's 5

**London**

1

# Jct **5**     Watford

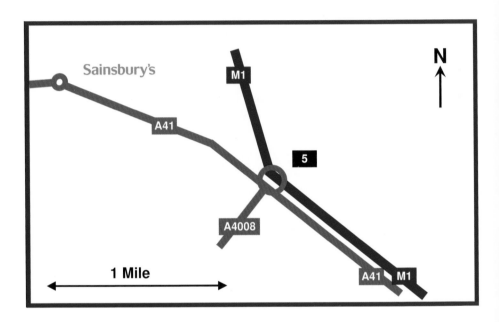

# Sainsbury's

**Opening Hours**

Dome Roundabout North     *Mon - Fri*     07:00 - 22:00
Western Avenue     *Sat*     07:00 - 22:00
Watford     *Sun*     10:00 - 16:00

Tel: 01923 680978

**Directions:**
Head North on A41 signposted Aylesbury. Store is on the right after 1 mile.

# Jct **11**    Dunstable

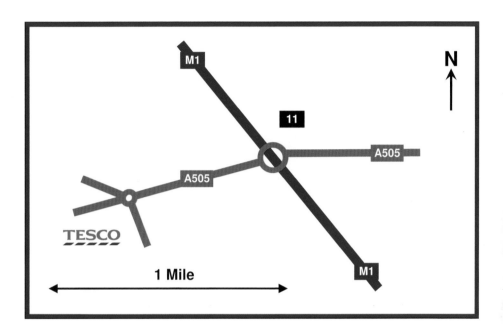

**TESCO**

|  |  | **Opening Hours** |
|---|---|---|
| Skimpot Road | **Mon - Fri** | 08:00 - 24 hr |
| Dunstable | **Sat** | 24 hr - 21:00 |
| Bedfordshire | **Sun** | 10:00 - 16:00 |

Tel: 01582 687500

**Directions:**
Travel west on A505 signposted Dunstable for ½ mile. The store is on the left after the first roundabout.

# Jct **21**      Leicester

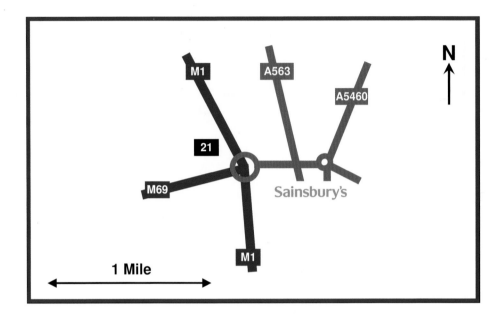

## Sainsbury's

Grove Farm Triangle
Enderby
Leicester

Tel: 01162 631153

| | Opening Hours |
|---|---|
| **Mon - Fri** | 08:00 - 22:00 |
| **Sat** | 07:00 - 22:00 |
| **Sun** | 10:00 - 16:00 |

**Directions:**
Head East on A5460 signposted Leicester. Store is on the right after ½ mile.

# Jct 33    Catcliffe

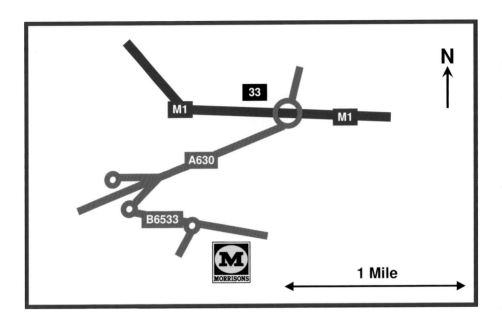

**Opening Hours**

Poplar Way

Catcliffe

| | | |
|---|---|---|
| | *Mon - Fri* | 08:30 - 20:00 |
| | *Sat* | 08:00 - 20:00 |
| | *Sun* | 10:00 - 16:00 |

Tel: 01709 839356

**Directions:**
Head south on A630 signposted Sheffield. Turn left after 1 mile onto B6533 towards Catcliffe. Continue across first roundabout and store is on the right.

# Jct 34     Sheffield Meadowhall

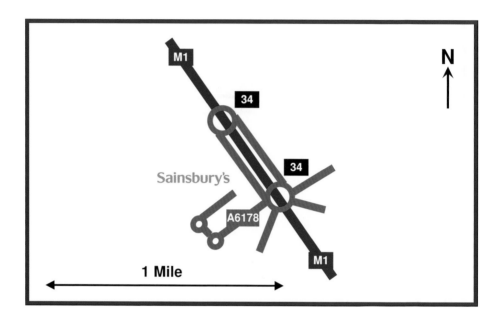

## Sainsbury's

|  | Opening Hours |  |
|---|---|---|
| Meadowhall Store | Mon - Fri | 07:00 - 22:00 |
| Meadowhall Centre | Sat | 07:00 - 20:00 |
| Sheffield | Sun | 11:00 - 17:00 |

Tel: 0114 256 8684

**Directions:**
Follow the signs to Meadowhall shopping centre. Store is on the left as you drive along Meadowhall Way.

# Jct **35**    Ecclesfield

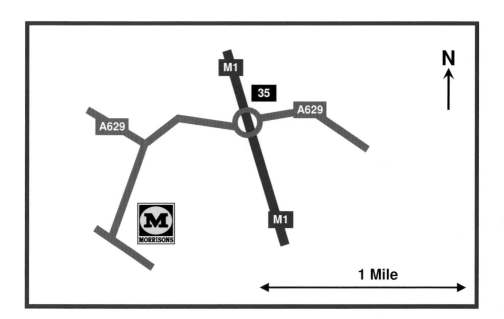

| | | **Opening Hours** |
|---|---|---|
| 299 The Common | **Mon - Fri** | 08:00 - 20:00 |
| Ecclesfield | **Sat** | 08:00 - 20:00 |
| | **Sun** | 10:00 - 16:00 |

Tel: 01142 456545

**Directions:**
Head west on A629 signposted Chapeltown. Turn left after 1/3 mile signposted Ecclesfield and proceed for 3/4 mile. Store is at the end of this road on the left.

7

# Jct **40**     **Wakefield**

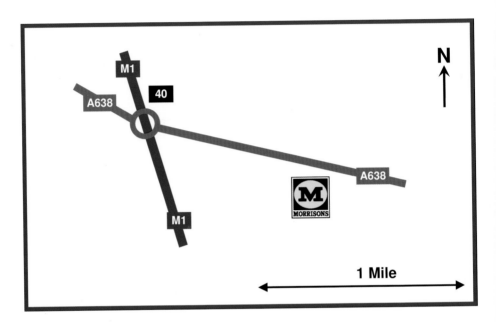

**MORRISONS**
Dewsbury Road
Wakefield

Tel: 01924 201655

**Opening Hours**

| | |
|---|---|
| *Mon - Fri* | 08:00 - 20:00 |
| *Sat* | 08:00 - 20:00 |
| *Sun* | 10:00 - 16:00 |

*Directions:*
Head east on A638 towards Wakefield. Store is 1 1/2 miles ahead.

# Jct 46    Leeds East

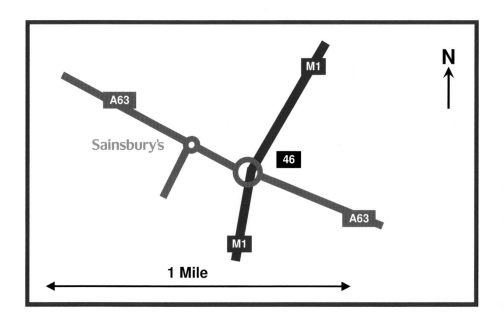

## Sainsbury's

Colton Retail Park
Stile Way
Leeds

Tel: 0113 232 8151

**Opening Hours**

| | |
|---|---|
| **Mon - Fri** | 07:00 - 22:00 |
| **Sat** | 07:00 - 22:00 |
| **Sun** | 11:00 - 17:00 |

*Directions:*
Head west on A63 signposted Leeds. Store is 1/3 mile on the left.

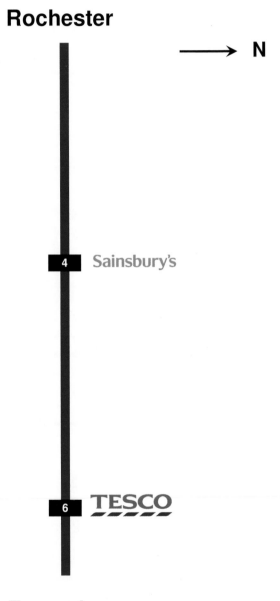

**Rochester**

**N**

4  Sainsbury's

6  TESCO

**Faversham**

# Jct **4**  Gillingham

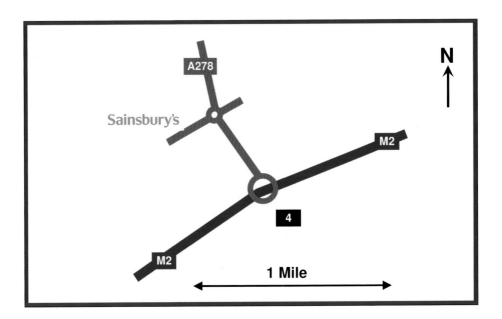

# Sainsbury's
**Opening Hours**

| | | |
|---|---|---|
| Hempstead Valley Shopping Centre | *Mon - Fri* | 08:00 - 22:00 |
| Hempstead | *Sat* | 07:00 - 22:00 |
| Gillingham | *Sun* | 10:00 - 16:00 |

Tel: 01634 382400

**Directions:**
Head north on A278 signposted Gillingham. Turn left at first roundabout.
Store is ¼ mile ahead on the right.

# Jct 6      Faversham

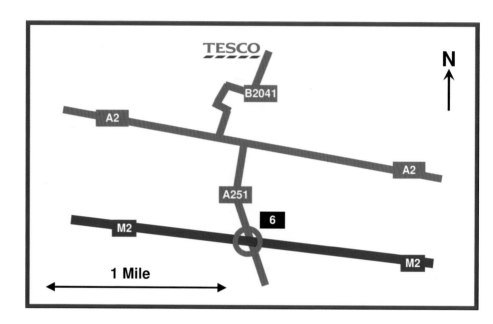

## TESCO

| | | Opening Hours |
|---|---|---|
| Crescent Road | Mon - Fri | 08:00 - 24 hr |
| Faversham | Sat | 24 hr - 21:00 |
| Kent | Sun | 10:00 - 16:00 |

Tel: 01795 567500

**Directions:**
Head north on A251 signposted Faversham. After ½ mile turn left at T-junction on A2 signposted Sittingbourne and then first right on B2041. Store is ¾ mile ahead on left after the railway station.

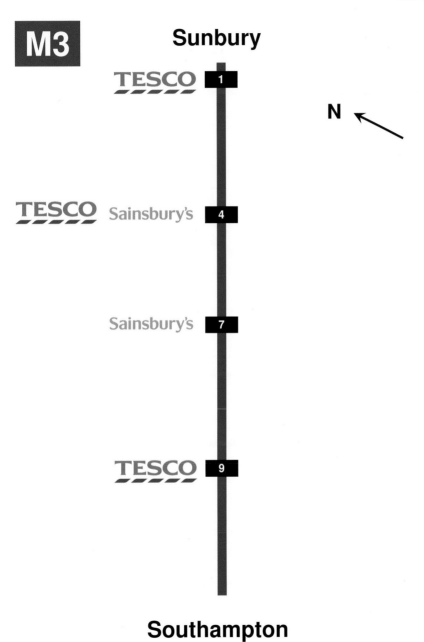

# Jct **1**     Sunbury

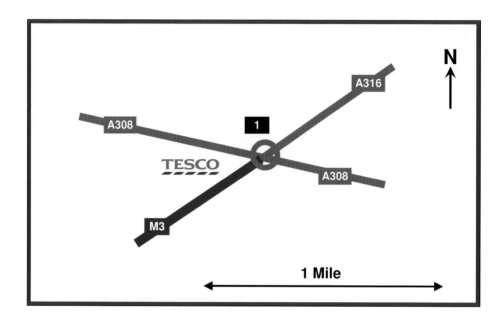

## TESCO

|  | **Opening Hours** | |
|---|---|---|
| Staines Road West | **Mon - Fri** | 07:30 - 22:00 |
| Sunbury on Thames | **Sat** | 07:30 - 22:00 |
| Middlesex | **Sun** | 10:00 - 16:00 |

Tel: 01932 747300

**Directions:**
Head west on A308 towards Staines. Store is immediately on the left.

# Jct **4**        Camberley

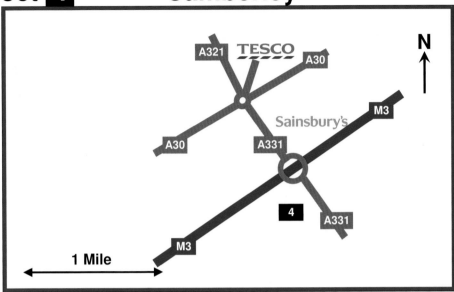

## Sainsbury's

Blackwater Valley Road
Camberley

| | Opening Hours |
|---|---|
| **Mon - Fri** | 07:00 - 23:00 |
| **Sat** | 07:00 - 22:00 |
| **Sun** | 10:00 - 16:00 |

Tel: 01276 676829

**Directions:**
Head north on A331 towards Camberley. Store is on the right after ½ mile.

## TESCO

The Meadows
Marshall Road
Sandhurst

| | Opening Hours |
|---|---|
| **Mon - Fri** | 08:00 - 24 hr |
| **Sat** | 24 hr - 21:00 |
| **Sun** | 10:00 - 16:00 |

Tel: 01276 895400

**Directions:**
Head north on A331 towards Camberley. After 1 ¼ miles take third exit into Tank Road. Store is immediately ahead.

# Jct **7**     Basingstoke

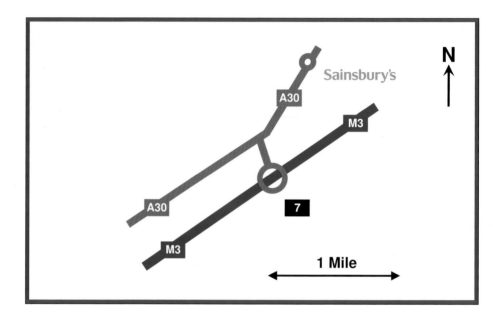

## Sainsbury's

|  | | **Opening Hours** |
|---|---|---|
| Wallop Drive | *Mon - Fri* | 07:00 - 22:00 |
| Hatch Warren | *Sat* | 07:00 - 22:00 |
| Basingstoke | *Sun* | 10:00 - 16:00 |

Tel: 01256 468405

**Directions:**
Head north on A278 towards Basingstoke. Turn left at first roundabout. Store is ¼ mile ahead on the right.

# Jct 9     Winchester

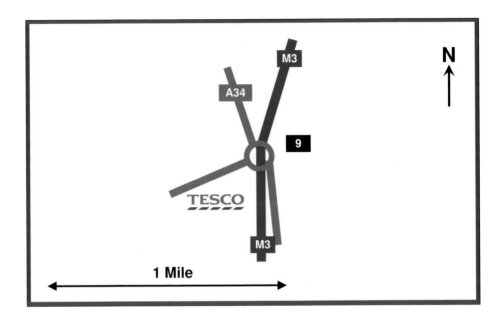

## TESCO

Opening Hours

| | | |
|---|---|---|
| Easton Lane | **Mon - Fri** | 08:00 - 24 hr |
| Winchester | **Sat** | 24 hr - 21:00 |
| Hampshire | **Sun** | 10:00 - 16:00 |

Tel: 01962 749400

**Directions:**
Head west from junction on Easton Lane towards Winchester town centre. Store is immediately on left.

**Wales**

⟶ **N**

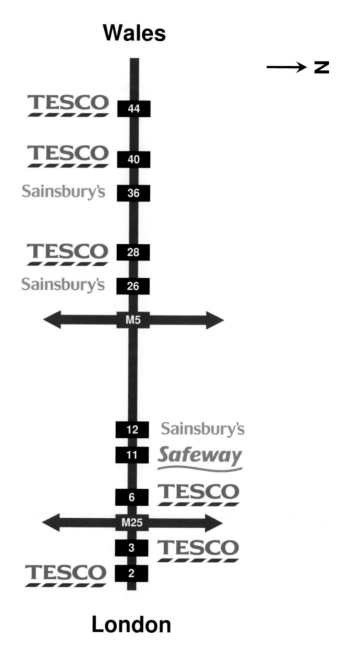

TESCO  44

TESCO  40

Sainsbury's  36

TESCO  28

Sainsbury's  26

⟷ M5

12  Sainsbury's

11  *Safeway*

6  TESCO

⟷ M25

3  TESCO

TESCO  2

**London**

18

# Jct **2**     Brentford, Isleworth

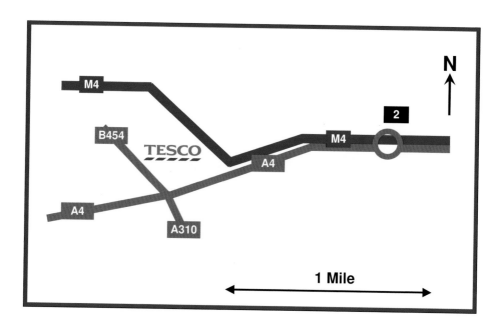

**TESCO**

Osterley Park
Syon Lane
Isleworth

Tel: 020 8258 7100

**Opening Hours**

| | | |
|---|---|---|
| *Mon - Fri* | 08:00 - 22:00 |
| *Sat* | 08:00 - 22:00 |
| *Sun* | 10:00 - 16:00 |

*Directions:*
Head west along A4 under M4 for 1 1/4 miles. At Gillette corner turn right into B454 Syon Lane. Store is on the right

# Jct **3**    Hayes

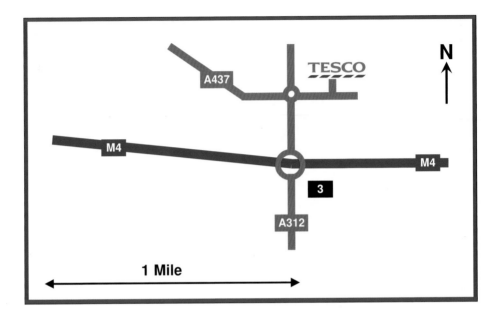

# TESCO

| | | **Opening Hours** |
|---|---|---|
| Bulls Bridge Industrial Estate | **Mon - Fri** | 08:00 - 24 hr |
| Hayes Road | **Sat** | 24 hr - 21:00 |
| Southall | **Sun** | 10:00 - 16:00 |

Tel: 020 8210 7100

**Directions:**
Head north on A312 towards Hayes / Yeading for 0.4 miles. Turn right at first roundabout into Hayes Road. Store is on left in Bulls Bridge Industrial Estate.

# Jct **6**       Slough

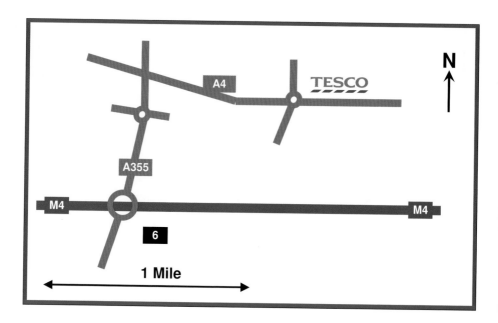

# TESCO

Brunel Way
Wellington St
Slough

Tel: 01753 227400

| | **Opening Hours** |
|---|---|
| **Mon - Fri** | 08:00 - 24 hr |
| **Sat** | 24 hr - 21:00 |
| **Sun** | 10:00 - 16:00 |

**Directions:**
Head north on A355 towards Slough for ¾ mile. Turn right on A4. Store is ¾ mile on left in Brunel Way after crossing a roundabout.

# Jct **11**  Reading

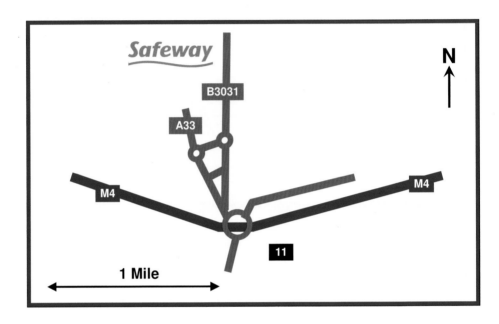

## Safeway

| | | **Opening Hours** |
|---|---|---|
| Rose Kiln Lane | **Mon - Fri** | 07:00 - 21:00 |
| Off Basingstoke Road | **Sat** | 07:00 - 20:00 |
| Reading | **Sun** | 10:00 - 16:00 |

Tel: 0118 9310357

**Directions:**
Take A33 North from junction towards Reading, then take immediate right onto B3031. Store is 1 mile ahead on the left.

# Jct **12**      **Reading West**

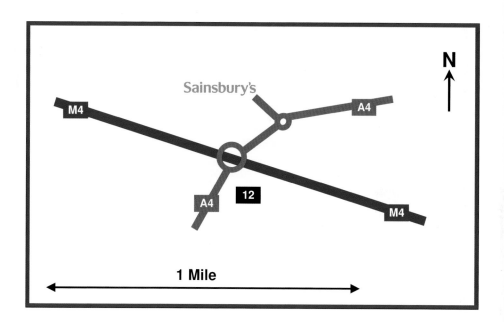

Sainsbury's

M4

A4

N

A4

**12**

M4

1 Mile

---

## Sainsbury's

A4 Bath Road
Calcot
Reading

Tel: 0118 938 2200

**Opening Hours**

| | |
|---|---|
| *Mon - Fri* | 07:00 - 00:00 |
| *Sat* | 06:00 - 22:00 |
| *Sun* | 10:00 - 16:00 |

***Directions:***
Head East on A4 signposted Reading. After ¼ mile turn left at first roundabout. Store is straight ahead.

# Jct 26     Newport

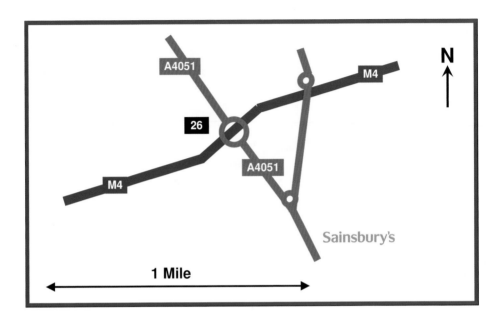

## Sainsbury's

Wyndham St
Newport

**Opening Hours**

| | |
|---|---|
| *Mon - Fri* | 08:00 - 21:00 |
| *Sat* | 07:00 - 20:00 |
| *Sun* | 10:00 - 16:00 |

Tel: 01633 265240

**Directions:**
Head south on A4051 towards Newport town centre. Store is ½ mile on the left.

# Jct **28**    Newport West

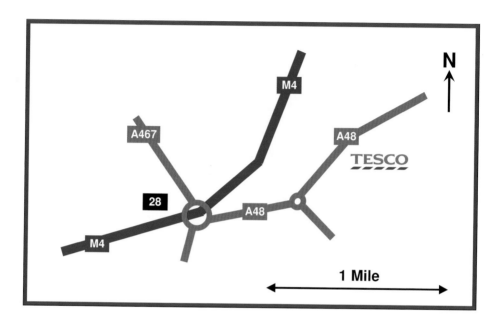

1 Mile

---

## TESCO

Harlech Retail Park
Cardiff Road
Newport

Tel: 01633 207600

**Opening Hours**

| | |
|---|---|
| *Mon - Fri* | 08:00 - 24 hr |
| *Sat* | 24 hr - 21:00 |
| *Sun* | 10:00 - 16:00 |

***Directions:***
Head east on A48 towards Newport. Continue on A48 at roundabout. Store is ½ mile ahead on the right in Harlech Retail Park on Cardiff Road.

# Jct **36**      **Bridgend**

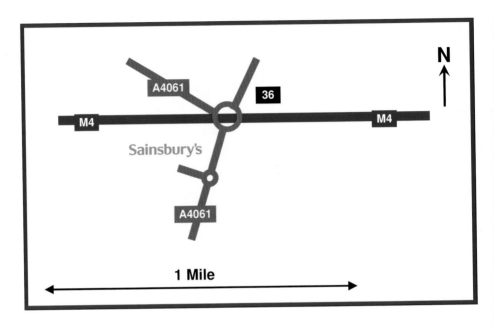

### Sainsbury's

### Sainsbury's

The Derwen
Bridgend

**Opening Hours**

| | |
|---|---|
| **Mon - Fri** | 07:00 - 22:00 |
| **Sat** | 07:00 - 22:00 |
| **Sun** | 10:00 - 16:00 |

Tel: 01656 648951

***Directions:***
Take A4061 south towards Bridgend. Store is on the right at the first roundabout.

# Jct 40     Port Talbot

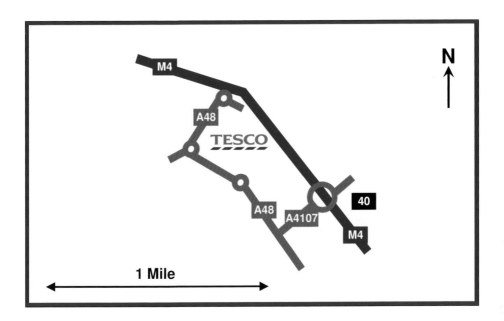

## TESCO

| | **Opening Hours** | |
|---|---|---|
| Heilborn Way | **Mon - Fri** | 08:00 - 24 hr |
| Prior St | **Sat** | 24 hr - 21:00 |
| Port Talbot | **Sun** | 10:00 - 16:00 |

Tel: 01639 667300

**Directions:**
Head south on A4107 signposted Port Talbot town centre. Turn right at T-junction onto A48. Turn right at third roundabout. Store is directly ahead in Prior Street.

# Jct **44**  Swansea East

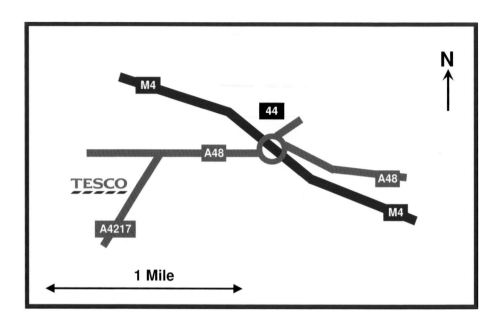

## TESCO

| | | **Opening Hours** |
|---|---|---|
| Nantyffin Road | **Mon - Fri** | 08:00 - 24 hr |
| Llansamlet | **Sat** | 24 hr - 21:00 |
| Swansea | **Sun** | 10:00 - 16:00 |

Tel: 01792 497400

**Directions:**

Head west on A48 towards Swansea. After 1 mile turn left onto A4217 towards Swansea. Store is shortly on the right in Nantyffin Road.

# Birmingham

Sainsbury's **2**

**TESCO** **7**

← **M50**

Sainsbury's **11a**

← **M4** →

**17** **M** MORRISONS

**16** **TESCO**

← **M49**

**TESCO** **20**

Sainsbury's **21**

Sainsbury's **25**

**TESCO** **30**

# Exeter

# Jct **2**

# Oldbury

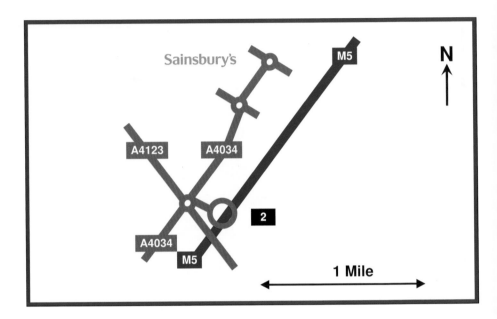

## Sainsbury's

Freeth Street
Oldbury

**Opening Hours**

| | |
|---|---|
| *Mon - Fri* | 08:00 - 22:00 |
| *Sat* | 07:00 - 22:00 |
| *Sun* | 10:00 - 16:00 |

Tel: 0121 665 2900

**Directions:**
Head north on A4034 for ¾ mile. Go straight across first roundabout into Halesowen Street. Turn left at next roundabout into Freeth Street. Store is on the left.

# Jct **7**    Worcester

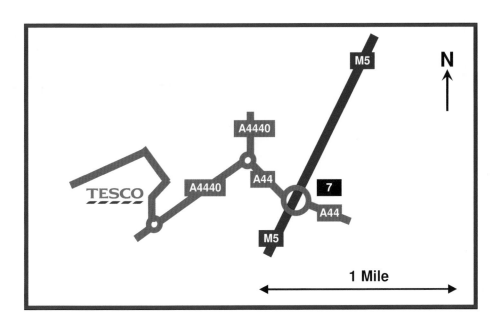

# TESCO

|  | | **Opening Hours** |
|---|---|---|
| St Peters Drive | **Mon - Fri** | 08:00 - 00:00 |
| Worcester | **Sat** | 08:00 - 00:00 |
| Worcestershire | **Sun** | 10:00 - 16:00 |

Tel: 01905 687400

**Directions:**
Head west on A44 for 1/2 mile towards Worcester. Turn left onto A4440 at first roundabout. Proceed for ¾ mile then turn right at next roundabout into St Peters Drive. Follow road for ½ mile. Store is on the left.

# Jct 11a     Gloucester

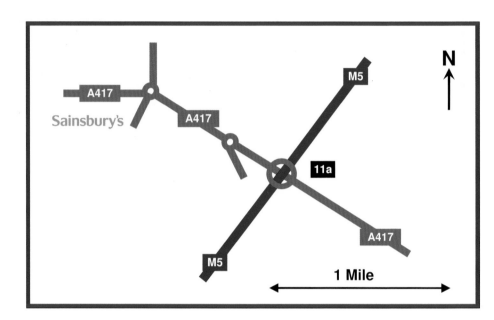

## Sainsbury's

Barnet Way
Barnwood
Gloucester

Tel: 01452 612673

**Opening Hours**
| | | |
|---|---|---|
| *Mon - Fri* | 07:00 - 22:00 |
| *Sat* | 07:00 - 22:00 |
| *Sun* | 10:00 - 16:00 |

*Directions:*
Head west on A417 for 1 mile towards Gloucester town centre. Turn left at second roundabout into Barnet Way. Take first right and store is ahead on the right.

# Jct **16**     **Bristol North**

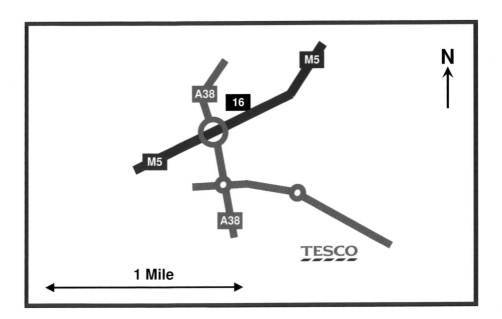

## TESCO

| | | **Opening Hours** |
|---|---|---|
| Bradley Stoke Centre | **Mon - Fri** | 08:00 - 24 hr |
| Bradley Stoke | **Sat** | 24 hr - 21:00 |
| Bristol | **Sun** | 10:00 - 16:00 |

Tel: 01454 847300

**Directions:**
Head south on A38 for ¼ mile towards Bristol. After ½ mile turn left at first roundabout towards Bradley Stoke. Go straight across next roundabout. Store is ½ mile ahead on the right in Bradley Stoke Centre.

# Jct **17**  Bristol North

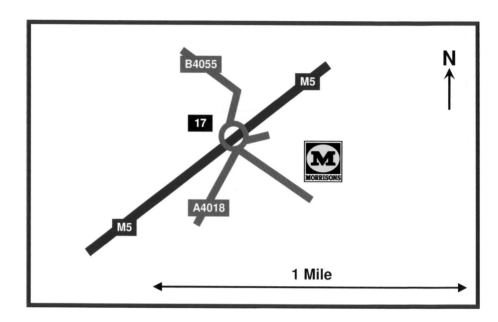

Lysander Road
Cribbs Causeway

**Opening Hours**

| | | |
|---|---|---|
| *Mon - Fri* | 08:30 - 20:00 |
| *Sat* | 08:00 - 20:00 |
| *Sun* | 10:00 - 16:00 |

Tel: 01179 509103

*Directions:*
Head south towards Cribbs Causeway. Store is 1/3 mile ahead.

# Jct **20**     Clevedon

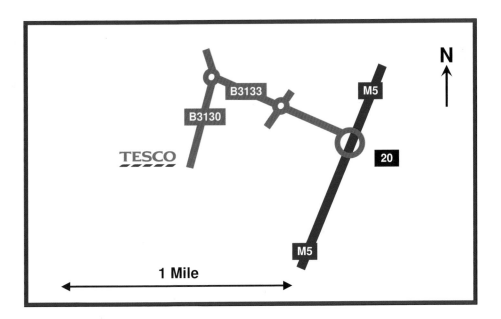

# TESCO
━━━━━

| | | **Opening Hours** |
|---|---|---|
| Kenn Road | **Mon - Fri** | 08:00 - 24 hr |
| Clevedon | **Sat** | 24 hr - 21:00 |
| Somerset | **Sun** | 10:00 - 16:00 |

Tel: 01275 517400

**Directions:**
After exiting motorway, proceed across first roundabout onto B3133 following signs for Clevedon. Turn left at next roundabout onto B3130. Store is ½ mile ahead.

# Jct **21** Weston-Super-Mare

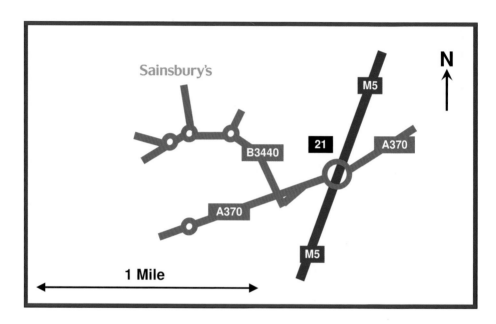

# Sainsbury's

**Opening Hours**

| | | |
|---|---|---|
| North Worle District Centre | *Mon - Fri* | 07:00 - 22:00 |
| Queensway | *Sat* | 07:00 - 21:00 |
| Worle | *Sun* | 10:00 - 16:00 |

Tel: 01934 510495

*Directions:*
Head west on A370 signposted Weston-Super-Mare. Leave this immediately by taking B3440. Proceed straight across first roundabout and then turn right at next. Store is ¼ mile ahead.

# Jct **25**   Taunton

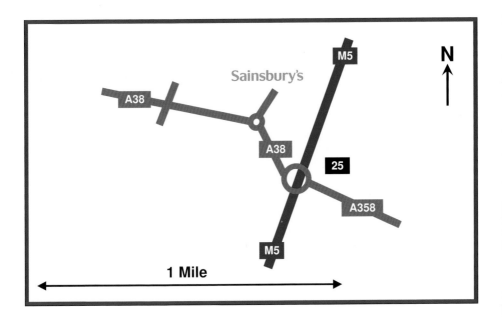

## Sainsbury's

Heron Gate
Bathpool
Taunton

**Opening Hours**

| | |
|---|---|
| *Mon - Fri* | 07:00 - 23:00 |
| *Sat* | 07:00 - 22:00 |
| *Sun* | 10:00 - 16:00 |

Tel: 01823 443163

**Directions:**
Head west on A38 towards Taunton. After 1/3 mile, turn right at first roundabout. Store is ¼ mile ahead.

# Jct 30    Exeter

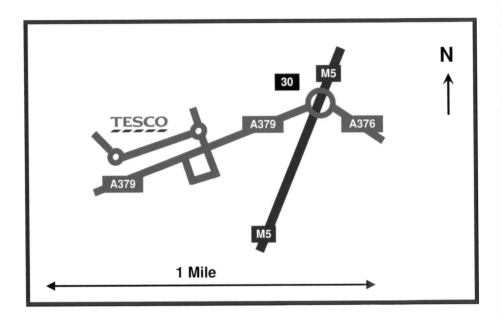

## TESCO

|  | | **Opening Hours** |
|---|---|---|
| Exeter Vale Shopping Centre | **Mon - Fri** | 08:00 - 24 hr |
| Russell Way | **Sat** | 24 hr - 21:00 |
| Exeter | **Sun** | 10:00 - 16:00 |
|  | Tel: 01392 607400 | |

**Directions:**
Head west on A379 for 1/2 mile towards Countess Wear. Take first left after passing under a railway bridge. Turn left at next roundabout. Store is ¼ mile ahead on the right in Exeter Vale Shopping Centre.

# Carlisle

**N**

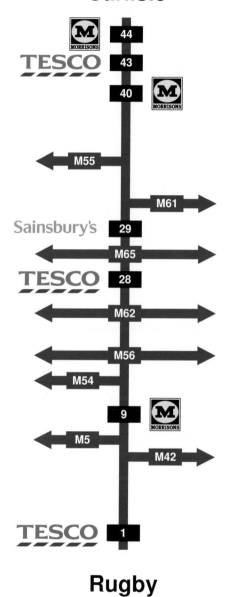

MORRISONS 44

TESCO 43

40 MORRISONS

M55

M61

Sainsbury's 29

M65

TESCO 28

M62

M56

M54

9 MORRISONS

M5

M42

TESCO 1

# Rugby

# Jct **1**     Rugby

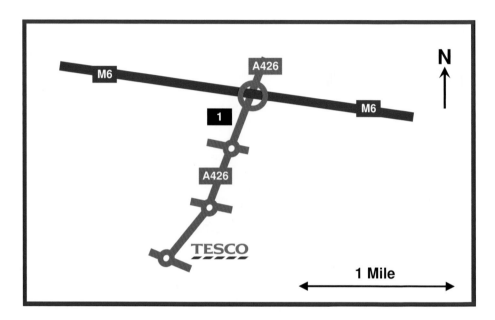

# TESCO

**Opening Hours**

1 Leicester Road

Rugby

Warwickshire

Tel: 01788 207400

| | | |
|---|---|---|
| *Mon - Fri* | 08:00 - 24 hr | |
| *Sat* | 24 hr - 21:00 | |
| *Sun* | 10:00 - 16:00 | |

*Directions:*
Head south on A426 towards Rugby for 1 1/2 miles. Store is on the left.

# Jct **9**    **Walsall**

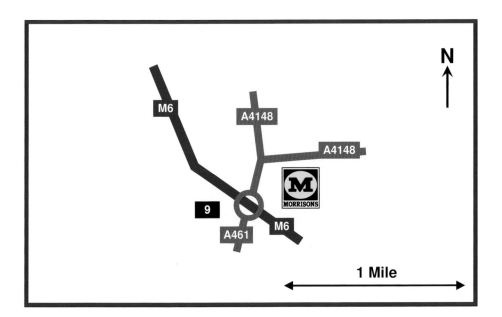

N

1 Mile

Wallows Lane
Walsall

**Opening Hours**

| | | |
|---|---|---|
| *Mon - Fri* | 08:30 - 20:00 |
| *Sat* | 08:00 - 20:00 |
| *Sun* | 10:00 - 16:00 |

Tel: 01922 616177

*Directions:*
Head north on A4148 towards Walsall. Store is 1/4 mile ahead on the right.

# Jct **28**     Leyland

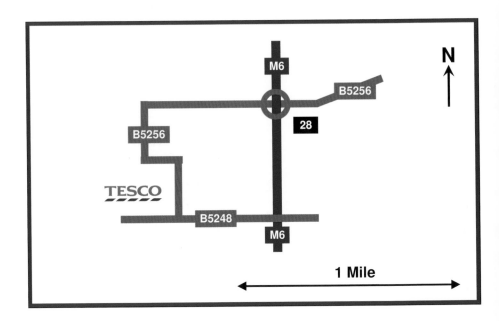

## TESCO

| | | **Opening Hours** |
|---|---|---|
| Towngate | **Mon - Fri** | 08:30 - 24 hr |
| Leyland | **Sat** | 24 hr - 22:00 |
| Preston | **Sun** | 11:00 - 17:00 |

Tel: 01772 407400

**Directions:**
Head west on B5256 towards Leyland town centre. After 1 mile turn right at the t-junction. Store is immediately on the right.

# Jct **29**         **Bamber Bridge**

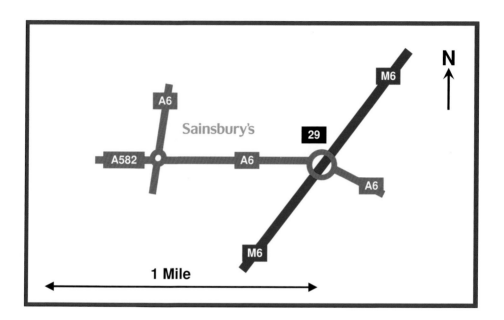

## Sainsbury's

Cuerden Way
Bamber Bridge
Preston

Tel: 01772 627762

**Opening Hours**

| | | |
|---|---|---|
| *Mon - Fri* | 08:00 - 22:00 |
| *Sat* | 07:00 - 22:00 |
| *Sun* | 10:00 - 16:00 |

***Directions:***
Head west on A6 towards Bamber Bridge. Store is ¾ mile on the right.

# Jct 40     Penrith

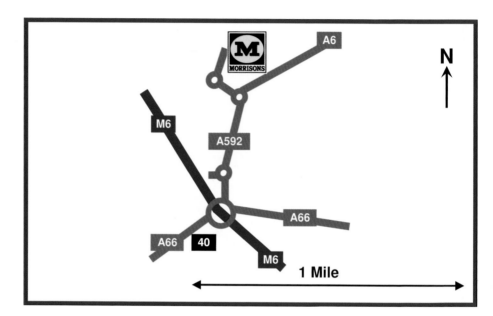

**MORRISONS**
Brunswick Road
Penrith

Tel: 01768 867631

**Opening Hours**

| | |
|---|---|
| *Mon - Fri* | 08:00 - 20:00 |
| *Sat* | 08:00 - 20:00 |
| *Sun* | 10:00 - 16:00 |

**Directions:**
Head north on A592 for 3/4 mile towards Penrith town centre. Turn left at second roundabout, then immediate right at next roundabout. Store is on the right.

# Jct 43     Carlisle

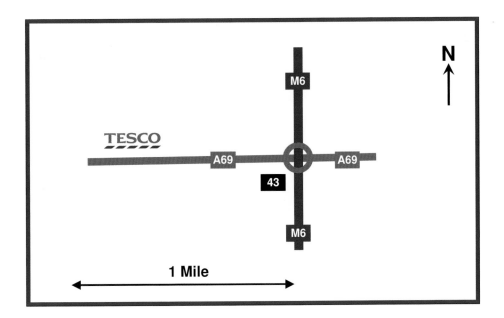

# TESCO

Warwick Road
Carlisle
Cumbria

Tel: 01228 600400

| | Opening Hours |
|---|---|
| **Mon - Fri** | 08:00 - 24 hr |
| **Sat** | 24 hr - 21:00 |
| **Sun** | 10:00 - 16:00 |

**Directions:**
Head west on A69 towards Carlisle. Store is located ¾ mile ahead in Warwick Road on the right.

# Jct **44**          Carlisle

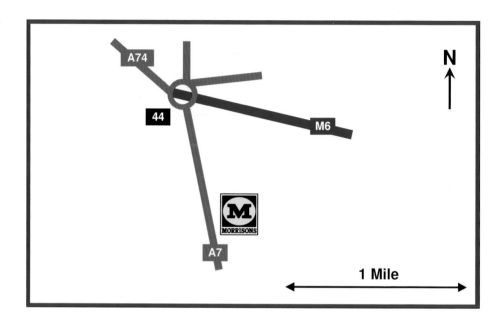

**MORRISONS**

Kingstown Road
Carlisle

**Opening Hours**

| | |
|---|---|
| *Mon - Fri* | 08:30 - 20:00 |
| *Sat* | 08:00 - 20:00 |
| *Sun* | 10:00 - 16:00 |

Tel: 01228 511771

**Directions:**
Head south on A7 towards Carlisle town centre. Store is on the left after 1 mile.

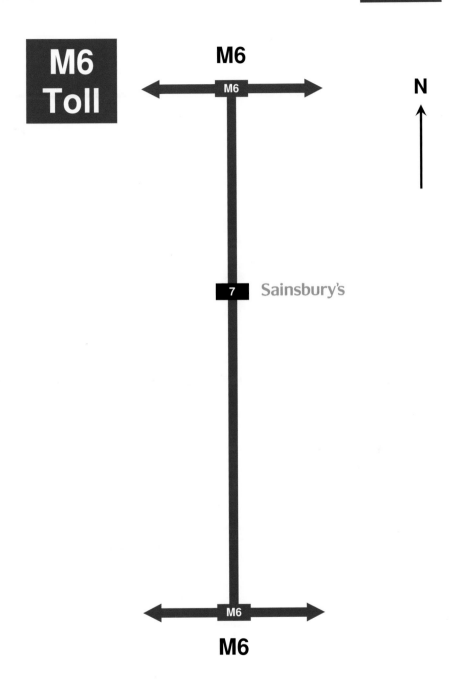

# Jct **7**        Cannock

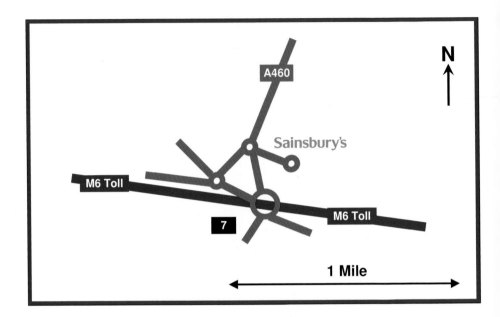

## Sainsbury's

Orbital Centre
Cannock

**Opening Hours**

| | | |
|---|---|---|
| **Mon - Fri** | 08:00 - 22:00 |
| **Sat** | 07:00 - 22:00 |
| **Sun** | 10:00 - 16:00 |

Tel: 01543 573757

**Directions:**
Head north on the A460 towards Cannock town centre. Store is immediately on the right in the Orbital Retail Centre.

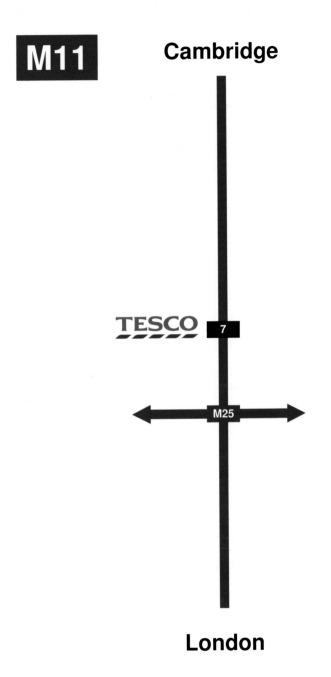

49

# Jct **7**     Harlow

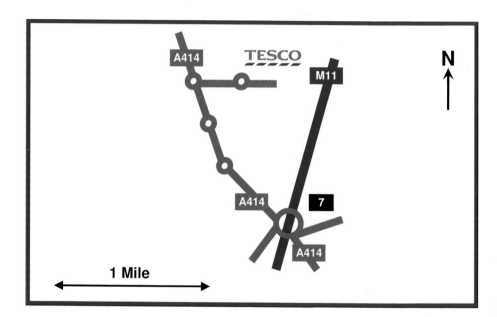

# TESCO

Church Langley Way
Harlow
Essex

Tel: 01279 697400

**Opening Hours**

| | |
|---|---|
| **Mon - Fri** | 08:00 - 24 hr |
| **Sat** | 24 hr - 21:00 |
| **Sun** | 10:00 - 16:00 |

**Directions:**
Head north on A414 towards Harlow for 1.5 miles. Turn right at third roundabout into Church Langley Way. Store is across next roundabout on the left.

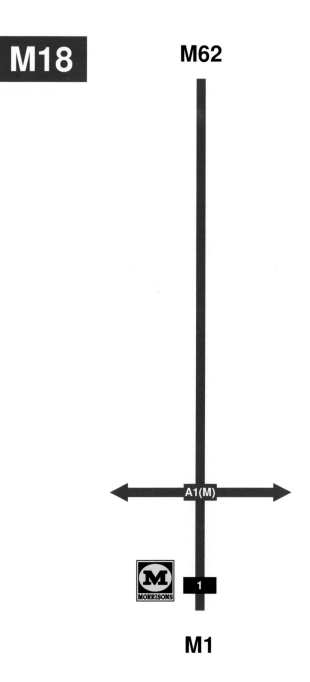

# Jct **1**  Rotherham East

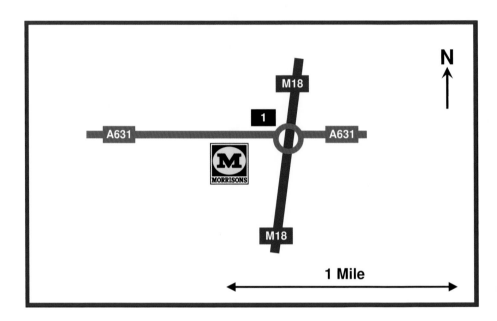

| | Opening Hours | |
|---|---|---|
| Bawtry Road | **Mon - Fri** | 08:00 - 20:00 |
| Bramley | **Sat** | 08:00 - 20:00 |
| | **Sun** | 10:00 - 16:00 |

Tel: 01709 540681

**Directions:**
Head west on A631 towards Rotherham. Store is 1/4 mile ahead on the left.

M20

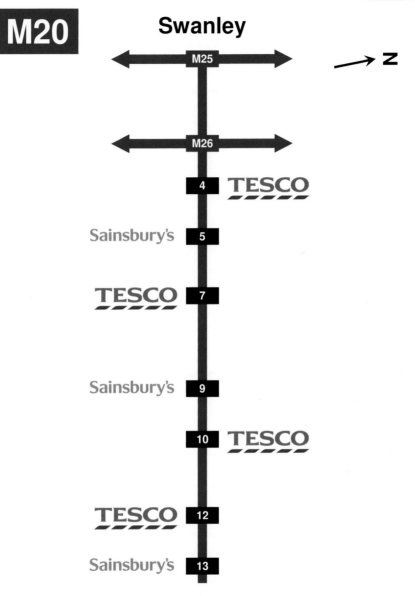

Swanley

M25

→ N

M26

4 TESCO

Sainsbury's 5

TESCO 7

Sainsbury's 9

10 TESCO

TESCO 12

Sainsbury's 13

Folkestone

# Jct **4**        Leybourne

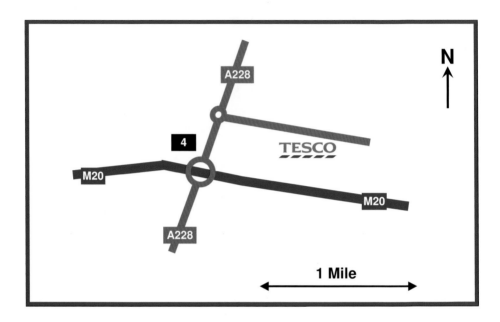

# TESCO

| | | **Opening Hours** |
|---|---|---|
| Lunsford Park | **Mon - Fri** | 08:00 - 24 hr |
| Larkfield | **Sat** | 24 hr - 21:00 |
| Aylesford | **Sun** | 10:00 - 16:00 |

Tel: 01622 701400

***Directions:***
Head north on A228 signposted Rochester. After 1/3 mile, turn right at first roundabout. Store is ½ mile ahead on right.

# Jct **5**     Maidstone

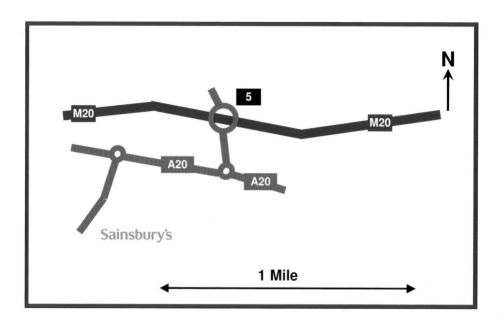

## Sainsbury's

| | Opening Hours | |
|---|---|---|
| Mills Wood Quarry Road | **Mon - Fri** | 06:00 - 22:00 |
| Aylesford | **Sat** | 06:00 - 22:00 |
| | **Sun** | 10:00 - 16:00 |

Tel: 01622 790223

**Directions:**
Head south for ¼ mile signposted Maidstone. Turn right at first roundabout towards Ditton. Proceed along A20 for ½ mile. Turn left at first roundabout. Store is 1/3 mile ahead on left.

# Jct **7**    Maidstone

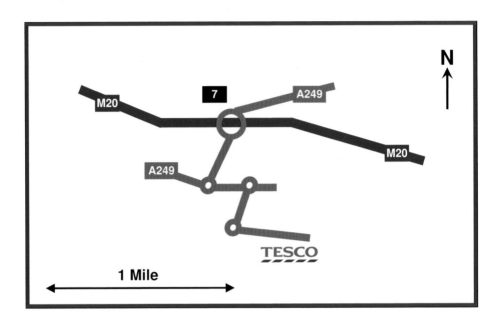

**1 Mile**

---

# TESCO
**Opening Hours**

| | | |
|---|---|---|
| Grovewood Drive | **Mon - Fri** | 08:00 - 24 hr |
| Weavering | **Sat** | 24 hr - 21:00 |
| Maidstone | **Sun** | 10:00 - 16:00 |

Tel: 01622 706400

**Directions:**
Head south on A249 towards Maidstone for 1/3 mile. Turn left at first roundabout signposted Bearsted and proceed for ¼ mile. Turn right at next roundabout into New Cut Road and proceed for ¼ mile. Turn left at next roundabout into Grovewood Drive. Store is 1/3 mile ahead on right.

# Jct 9     Ashford

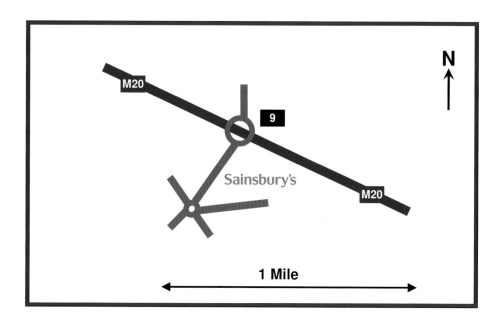

# Sainsbury's

Simone Weil Avenue
Ashford

**Opening Hours**

| | |
|---|---|
| **Mon - Fri** | 06:00 - 00:00 |
| **Sat** | 06:00 - 22:00 |
| **Sun** | 10:00 - 16:00 |

Tel: 01233 610841

**Directions:**
Head south towards Ashford town centre for 1/3 mile. At first roundabout, take first left (Simone Weil Avenue). Store is 1/3 mile on left.

# Jct **10**    Ashford East

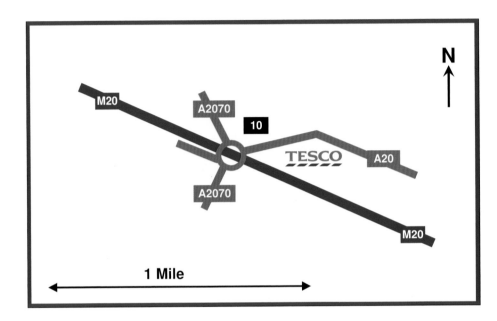

1 Mile

---

**TESCO**

Hythe Road
Wilesborough
Ashford

Tel: 01233 207400

**Opening Hours**

| | |
|---|---|
| *Mon - Fri* | 08:00 - 24 hr |
| *Sat* | 24 hr - 21:00 |
| *Sun* | 10:00 - 16:00 |

**Directions:**
Take A20 east turn from junction towards Sellindge and Hythe. Store is immediately on the right.

# Jct 12     Folkestone

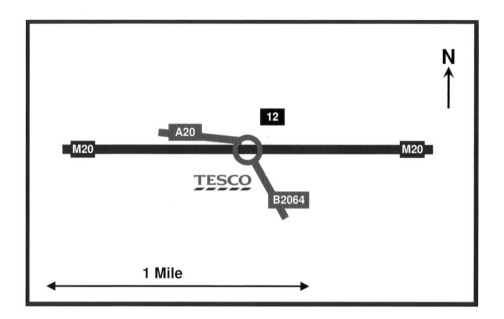

# Jct **13**     Folkestone

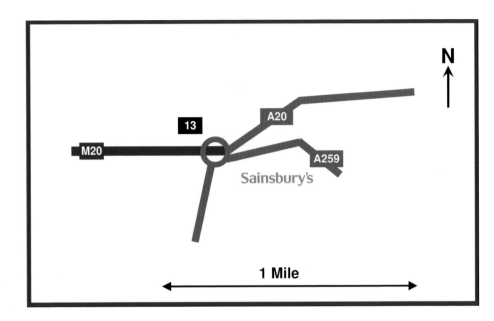

# Sainsbury's

| | | **Opening Hours** |
|---|---|---|
| Park Farm Industrial Estate | **Mon - Fri** | 06:00 - 22:00 |
| Park Farm Road | **Sat** | 06:00 - 22:00 |
| Folkestone | **Sun** | 10:00 - 16:00 |

Tel: 01303 850810

**Directions:**
Take A259 east. Store is ¼ mile on the right.

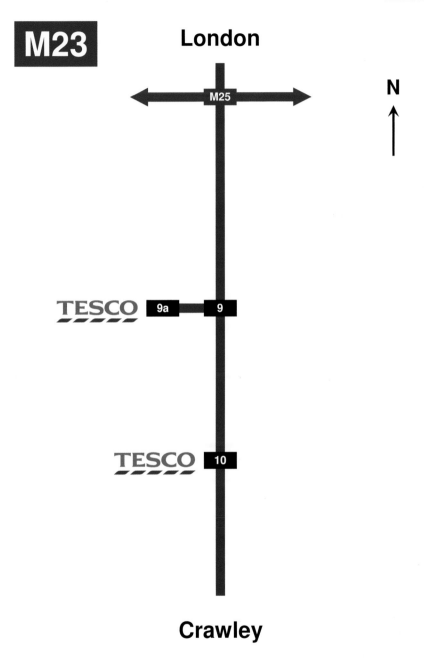

# Jct **9a**   Horley / Gatwick Airport

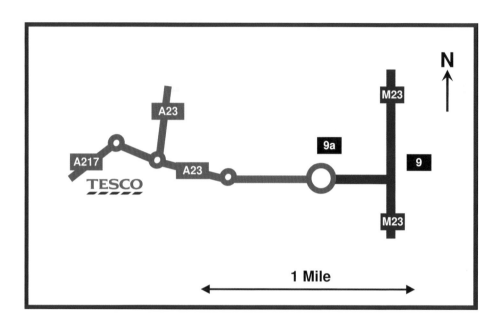

**TESCO**

| | **Opening Hours** | |
|---|---|---|
| Reigate Road | **Mon - Fri** | 08:00 - 24 hr |
| Hookwood | **Sat** | 24 hr - 21:00 |
| Horley | **Sun** | 10:00 - 16:00 |

Tel: 01293 727400

**Directions:**
Proceed across the roundabout at junction 9a. Continue heading west for 1 mile on A23 towards Redhill. At junction with A217 continue straight across and proceed along A217 towards Reigate. Cross another roundabout and store is on the left in Reigate Road.

# Jct **10**     Crawley

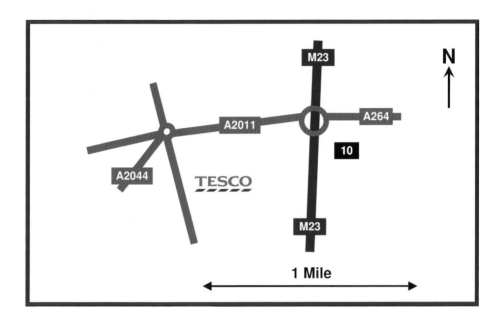

1 Mile

# TESCO

| | | **Opening Hours** |
|---|---|---|
| Hazelwick Avenue | **Mon - Fri** | 08:00 - 24 hr |
| Crawley | **Sat** | 24 hr - 21:00 |
| West Sussex | **Sun** | 10:00 - 16:00 |

Tel: 01293 728400

**Directions:**
Head west along A2011 for 1 mile towards Crawley. Turn left at roundabout into Hazelwick avenue. Store is ¼ mile ahead on the left.

# M25

## London Orbital

N

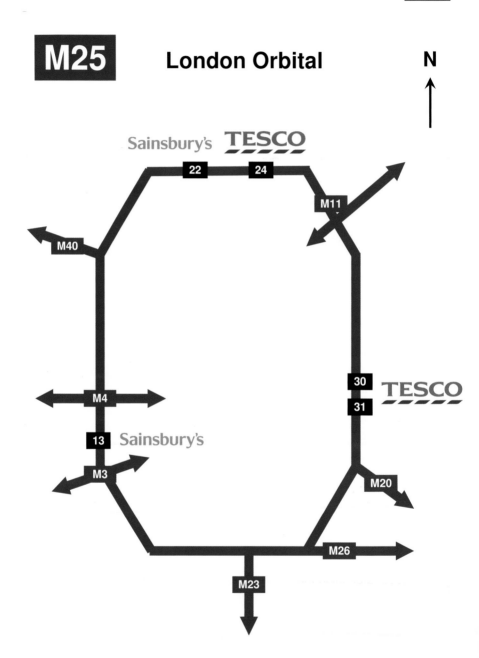

# Jct **13**     **Staines**

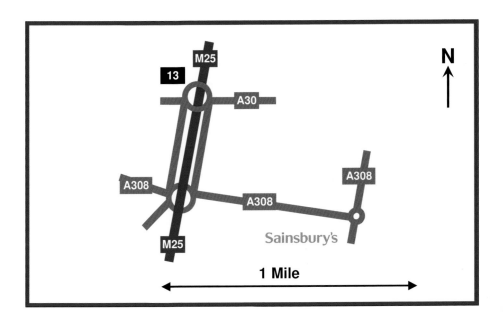

## Sainsbury's

The Causeway
Staines

**Opening Hours**

| | |
|---|---|
| **Mon - Fri** | 07:00 - 21:00 |
| **Sat** | 07:00 - 21:00 |
| **Sun** | 10:00 - 16:00 |

Tel: 01784 456644

**Directions:**
Head south alongside motorway for 2/3 mile. Turn left onto A308 and head east towards Staines for another 2/3 mile. Turn right at first roundabout and store is immediately on the right.

# Jct **22**     London Colney

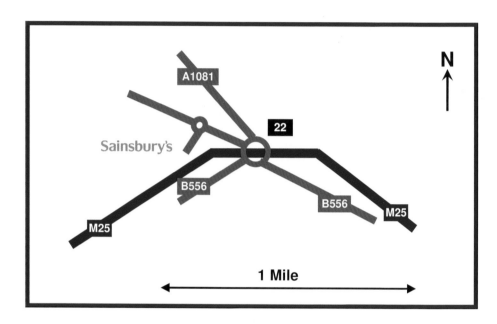

## Sainsbury's

Barnet Road
London Colney
St Albans

Tel: 01727 744400

**Opening Hours**

| | |
|---|---|
| *Mon - Fri* | 07:00 - 22:00 |
| *Sat* | 07:00 - 22:00 |
| *Sun* | 11:00 - 17:00 |

***Directions:***
Clockwise, take first left then left again. Store is 1/4 mile ahead in retail park.

Anti-clockwise, cross over the motorway and take the first left then left again. Store is ¼ mile ahead in retail park.

# Jct 24    Potters Bar

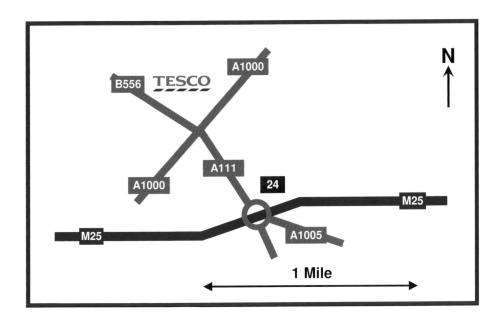

## TESCO

Mutton Lane
Potters Bar
Hertfordshire

Tel: 01707 347500

**Opening Hours**

| | |
|---|---|
| *Mon - Fri* | 08:00 - 24 hr |
| *Sat* | 24 hr - 21:00 |
| *Sun* | 10:00 - 16:00 |

**Directions:**
Head north on A111 towards Potters Bar for 3/4 mile. Proceed across A1000 into B556 towards South Mimms and store is on the right.

# Jct **30**   Thurrock / Lakeside

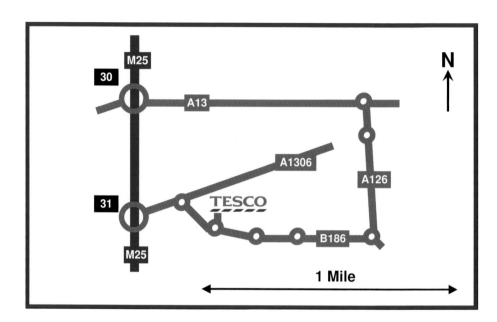

## TESCO

| | | **Opening Hours** |
|---|---|---|
| Cygnet View | **Mon - Fri** | 08:00 - 24 hr |
| Lakeside | **Sat** | 24 hr - 21:00 |
| Grays | **Sun** | 10:00 - 16:00 |

Tel: 01708 791400

**Directions:**
Clockwise, from Junction 30, head east along A13 and then follow signs to Lakeside shopping centre. Turn right into Cygnet view at the third roundabout on B186.

Anti-clockwise from junction 31, head east on A1306. Turn right at first roundabout into B186 and then left at the next roundabout into Cygnet View.

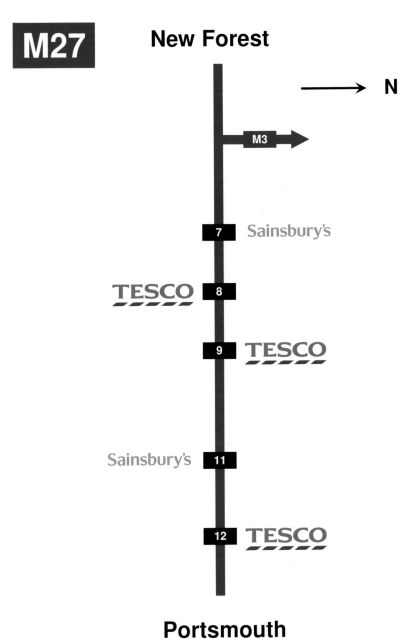

# Jct **7**     Southampton

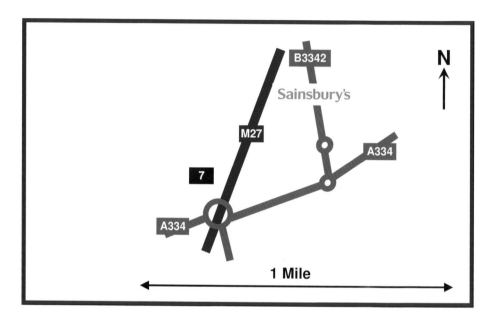

## Sainsbury's

Tollbar Way
Hedge End
Southampton

Tel: 01489 790452

**Opening Hours**

| | |
|---|---|
| *Mon - Fri* | 07:00 - 23:00 |
| *Sat* | 07:00 - 22:00 |
| *Sun* | 10:00 - 16:00 |

***Directions:***
Head east on A334 towards Wickham. After 1/3 mile turn left at first roundabout onto B3342. Store is 1/4 mile ahead on the left.

# Jct 8      Bursledon

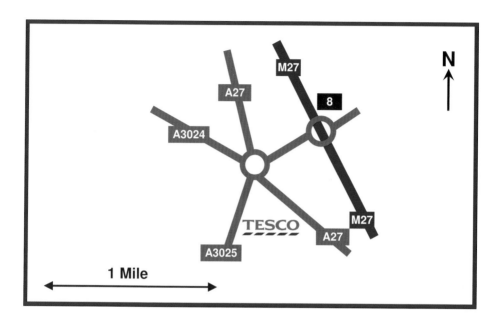

## TESCO

| | | Opening Hours |
|---|---|---|
| Hamble Lane | Mon - Fri | 08:00 - 24 hr |
| Bursledon | Sat | 24 hr - 21:00 |
| Southampton | Sun | 10:00 - 16:00 |

Tel: 023 8029 7500

**Directions:**
Head west on A3024 towards Southampton for 1/4 mile. Take second exit from roundabout, into Hamble Lane. Store is on the left.

# Jct **9**   Whiteley Outlet Village

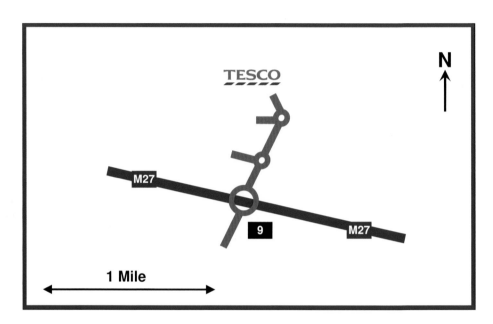

## TESCO

| | | **Opening Hours** |
|---|---|---|
| Whiteley Village | **Mon - Fri** | 08:00 - 24 hr |
| Whiteley Way | **Sat** | 24 hr - 21:00 |
| Fareham | **Sun** | 10:00 - 16:00 |

Tel: 01489 722400

**Directions:**
Head north towards Swanwick and proceed straight across two roundabouts, following signs to Whiteley Shopping Village.

# Jct **11**　　　**Fareham**

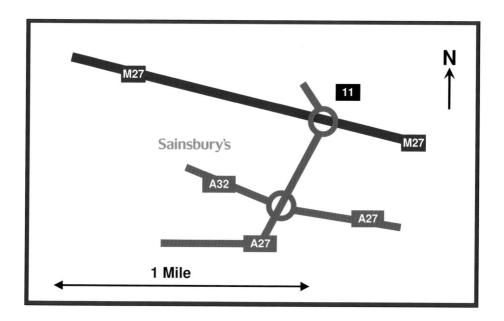

# Sainsbury's

Wallington Way
Broadcut
Fareham

Tel: 01329 827936

| Opening Hours | |
| --- | --- |
| **Mon - Fri** | 07:00 - 23:00 |
| **Sat** | 07:00 - 22:00 |
| **Sun** | 10:00 - 16:00 |

**Directions:**
Head south from motorway towards Fareham town centre. After 1/2 mile leave the road and turn right onto A32. Proceed along A32 for 1/2mile and store is on the right.

# Jct **12**     Portsmouth

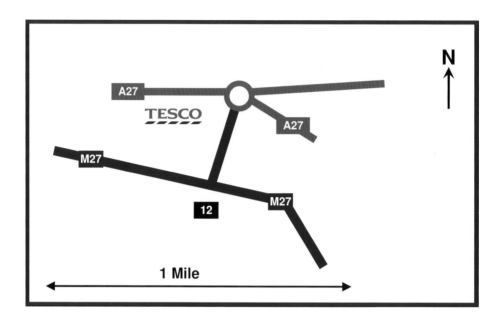

# TESCO

| | | **Opening Hours** |
|---|---|---|
| Clement Atlee Way | **Mon - Fri** | 08:00 - 24 hr |
| Portsmouth | **Sat** | 24 hr - 21:00 |
| Hampshire | **Sun** | 10:00 - 16:00 |

Tel: 023 9230 7800

**Directions:**
Exit motorway and turn first left at roundabout onto the A27 signposted
Fareham . Store is immediately on the left in Clement Atlee Way.

74

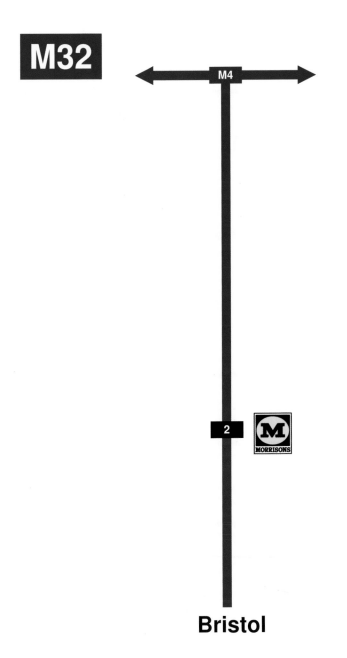

M32

M4

2

N

Bristol

# Jct **2**    **Bristol Fishponds**

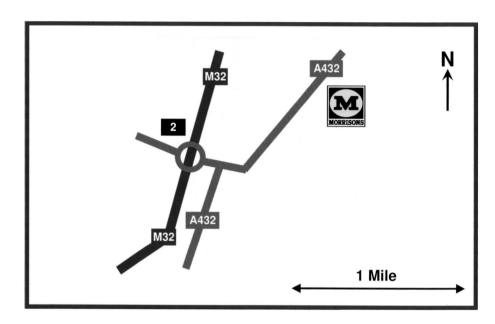

**MORRISONS**

668-718 Fishponds Road
Bristol

**Opening Hours**

| | | |
|---|---|---|
| *Mon - Fri* | 08:30 - 20:00 |
| *Sat* | 08:00 - 20:00 |
| *Sun* | 10:00 - 16:00 |

Tel: 01179 586147

*Directions:*
Head east from the junction on the A432. Store is 1 1/2 miles ahead on the right.

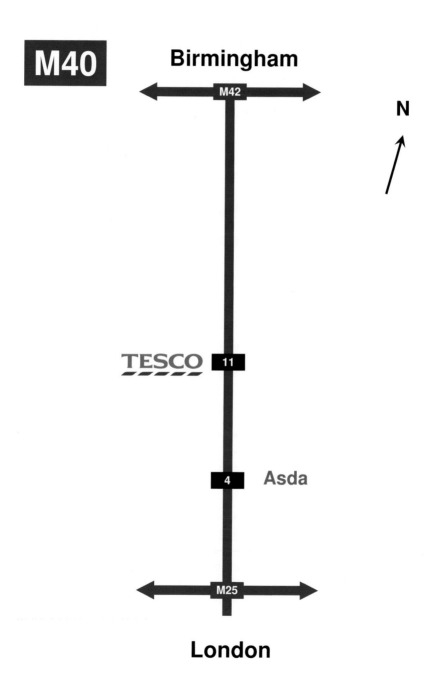

# Jct 4       High Wycombe

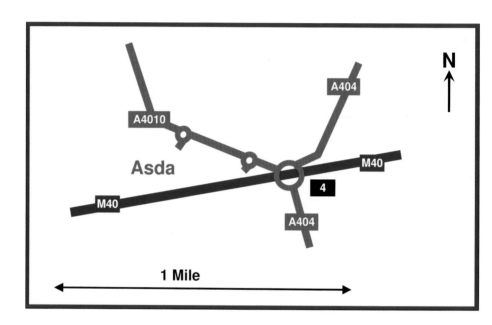

## Asda

Holmers Farm Way
High Wycombe

**Opening Hours**

| | |
|---|---|
| *Mon - Fri* | 07:30 - 22:00 |
| *Sat* | 07:30 - 22:00 |
| *Sun* | 10:00 - 16:00 |

Tel: 01494 441611

*Directions:*
Head west on A4010 towards West Wycombe. Turn left at second
roundabout. Store is directly ahead.

# Jct **11**     **Banbury**

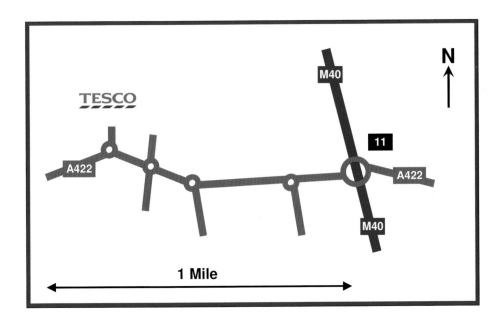

## TESCO

| | **Opening Hours** | |
|---|---|---|
| Lockheed Close | **Mon - Fri** | 08:00 - 24 hr |
| Banbury | **Sat** | 24 hr - 21:00 |
| Oxfordshire | **Sun** | 10:00 - 16:00 |

Tel: 01295 457400

**Directions:**
Head west on A422 towards Banbury. Proceed for a mile across 3 roundabouts and then turn right at the fourth into Lockheed Close. The store is immediately ahead.

**M42**

**M42**

**Tamworth**

 N

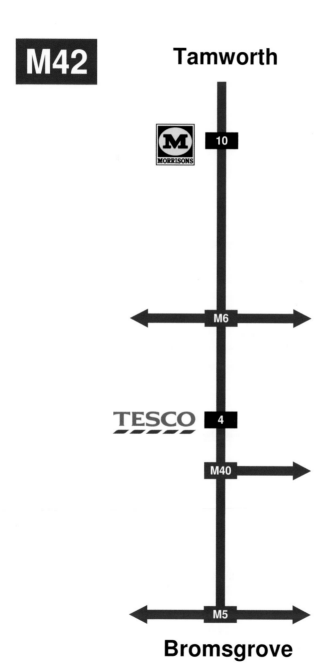

| 10 |

| M6 |

TESCO | 4 |

| M40 |

| M5 |

**Bromsgrove**

# Jct **4**  Solihull

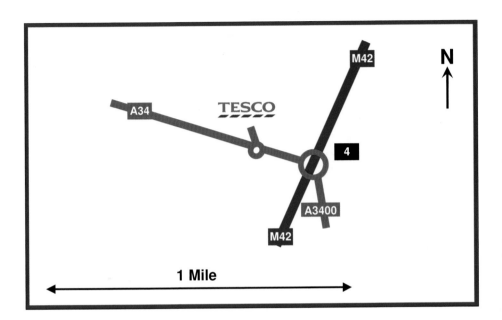

# TESCO

|  | **Opening Hours** |  |
|---|---|---|
| 1505 Stratford Road | **Mon - Fri** | 08:00 - 24 hr |
| Shirley | **Sat** | 24 hr - 21:00 |
| Solihull | **Sun** | 10:00 - 16:00 |

Tel: 0121 253 7500

**Directions:**
Head northwest on A34 towards Birmingham and Shirley. Almost immediately turn right at first roundabout. Store is straight ahead.

# Jct **10**    Tamworth

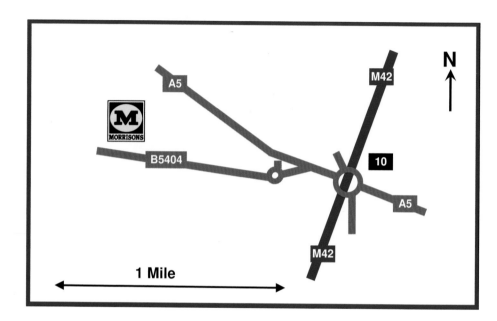

**MORRISONS**

Hilmore Way
Tamworth

Tel: 01827 284082

**Opening Hours**
| | |
|---|---|
| **Mon - Fri** | 08:30 - 20:00 |
| **Sat** | 08:00 - 20:00 |
| **Sun** | 10:00 - 16:00 |

*Directions:*
Head west on A5 towards Tamworth for 1/4 mile. Leave the A5 and take the B5404. Continue heading west for 1 mile. Store is on the right.

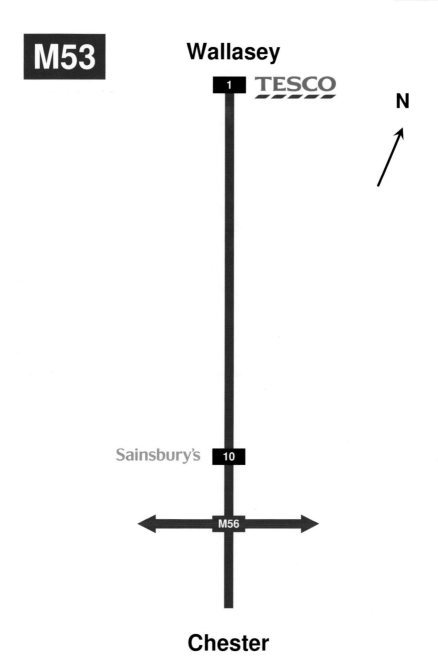

# Jct **1**    Wallasey

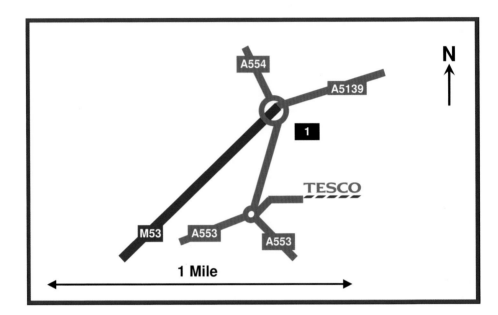

# TESCO

Bidston Link Road
Birkenhead
Merseyside

Tel: 0151 801 7600

**Opening Hours**

| | |
|---|---|
| *Mon - Fri* | 08:00 - 24 hr |
| *Sat* | 24 hr - 21:00 |
| *Sun* | 10:00 - 16:00 |

*Directions:*
Head south on A553 towards Birkenhead for 1/4 mile. Turn left at first roundabout into Bidston Link Road. Store is at the end on the left.

# Jct 10     Ellesmere Port

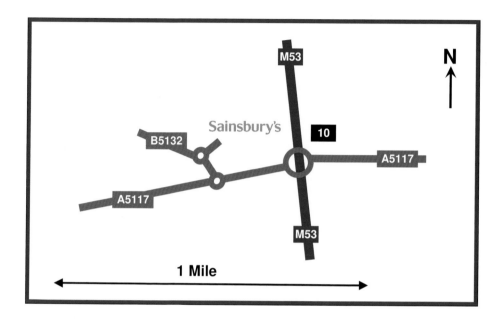

## Sainsbury's

| | **Opening Hours** |
|---|---|
| Kinsey Road | **Mon - Fri** 08:00 - 22:00 |
| Little Stanney | **Sat** 08:00 - 22:00 |
| Ellesmere Port | **Sun** 10:30 - 16:30 |

Tel: 0151 357 3181

**Directions:**
Head west on A5117 signposted Stanney Woods Country Park for 1/4 mile. Turn right at first roundabout onto B5132. Turn right at next roundabout and store is directly ahead.

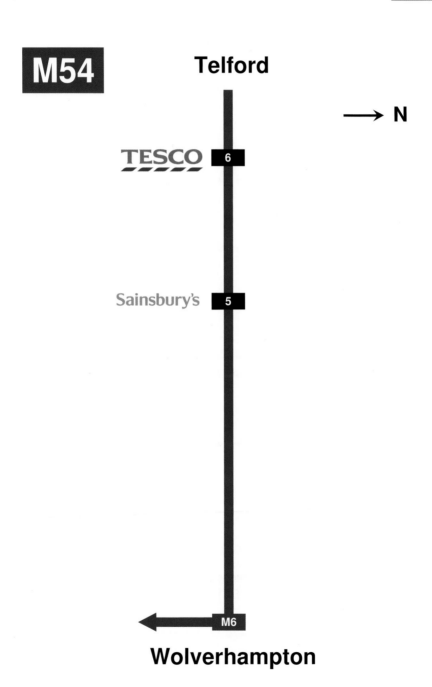

# Jct **5**    **Telford**

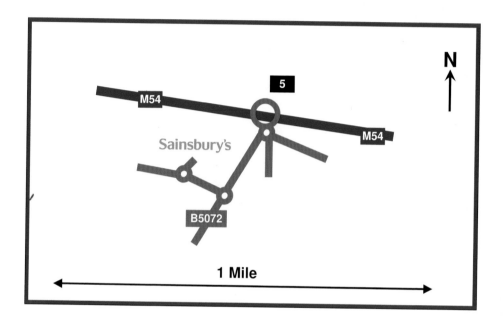

## Sainsbury's

Colliers Way
Telford

**Opening Hours**

| | |
|---|---|
| **Mon - Fri** | 08:00 - 22:00 |
| **Sat** | 07:30 - 22:00 |
| **Sun** | 10:00 - 16:00 |

Tel: 01952 299702

**Directions:**
Take B5072 exit south from motorway junction towards town centre. Turn right at first roundabout. Cross second roundabout and turn right at third. Store is immediately ahead.

# Jct **6**   **Telford**

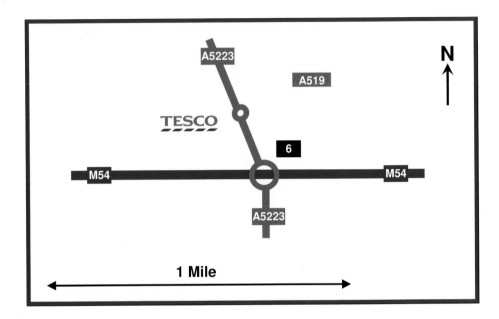

# TESCO

Wrekin Retail Park
Arleston
Telford

Tel: 01952 656400

**Opening Hours**

| | |
|---|---|
| *Mon - Fri* | 08:00 - 24 hr |
| *Sat* | 24 hr - 21:00 |
| *Sun* | 10:00 - 16:00 |

**Directions:**
Head north on A5223 towards Hadley. Store is 1/4 mile on the left in Wrekin retail park.

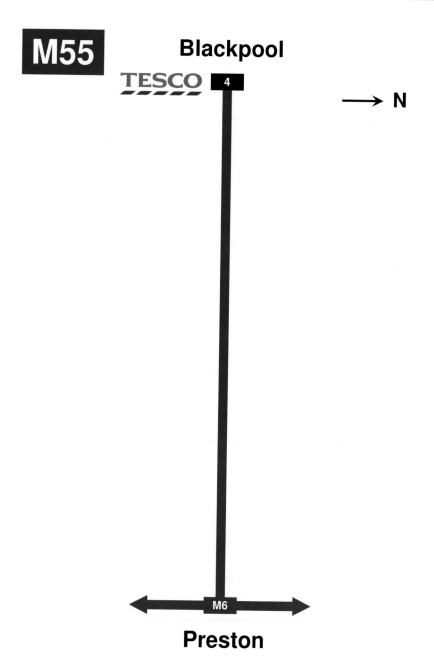

# Jct **4**     **Blackpool**

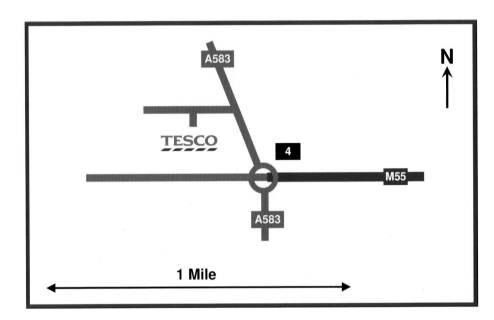

## TESCO

**Opening Hours**

| | | |
|---|---|---|
| Clifton Retail Park | **Mon - Fri** | 08:00 - 24 hr |
| Clifton Road | **Sat** | 24 hr - 21:00 |
| Blackpool | **Sun** | 10:00 - 16:00 |

Tel: 01253 617500

**Directions:**
Head north on A583 towards Blackpool town centre. Take first left after 1/4 mile into Clifton Road. Store is 1/4 mile ahead on the left.

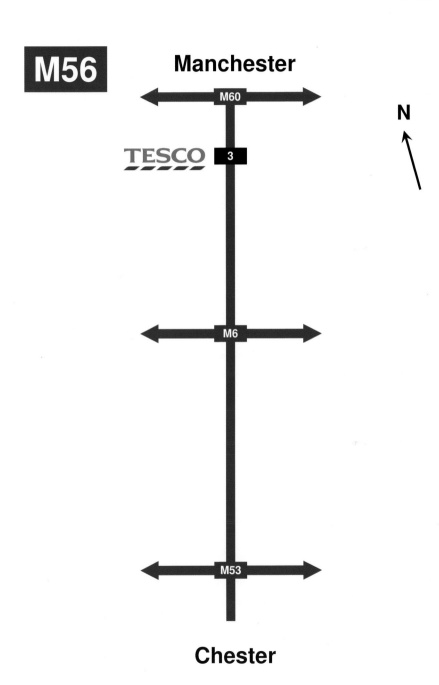

# Jct 3   Baguley

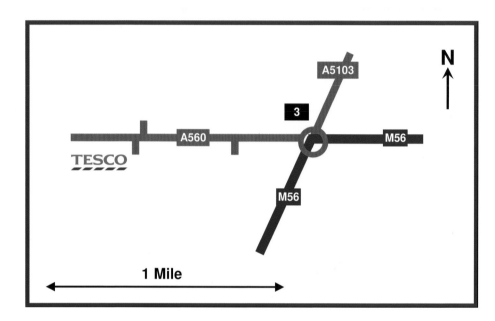

**1 Mile**

# TESCO

**Opening Hours**

| | | |
|---|---|---|
| Altrincham Road | **Mon - Fri** | 08:00 - 24 hr |
| Baguley | **Sat** | 24 hr - 21:00 |
| Greater Manchester | **Sun** | 10:00 - 16:00 |

Tel: 0161 251 7600

**Directions:**
Head west on A560 signposted Altrincham. Store is 1 mile ahead on the left.

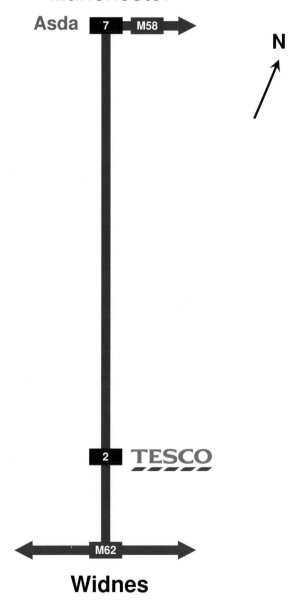

# Jct **2**     Prescot

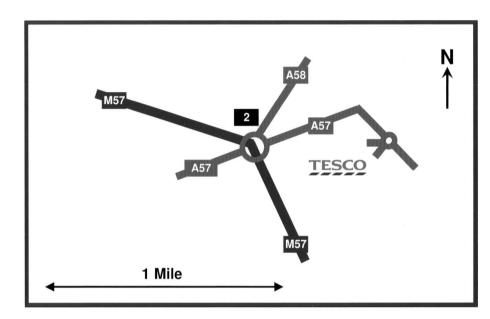

## TESCO

**Opening Hours**

Cables Retail Park | **Mon - Fri** | 08:00 - 24 hr
Steley Way | **Sat** | 24 hr - 21:00
Prescot | **Sun** | 10:00 - 16:00

Tel: 01518 011300

*Directions:*
Head east on A57 towards Prescot. Keep on A57 and after 1 mile at roundabout turn right into Cables Retail Park. Store is straight ahead.

# Jct **7**     Aintree

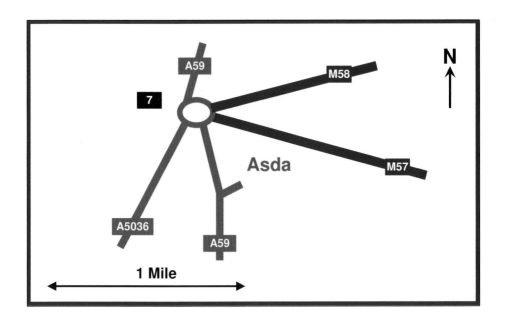

# Asda

Ormskirk Road
Aintree
Liverpool

Tel: 0151 531 7778

***Opening Hours***

| | | |
|---|---|---|
| ***Mon - Fri*** | 08:30 - 22:00 |
| ***Sat*** | 24hr - 22:00 |
| ***Sun*** | 10:30 - 16:30 |

***Directions:***
Head south on A59 towards Liverpool centre. Store is 1/4 mile on the left.

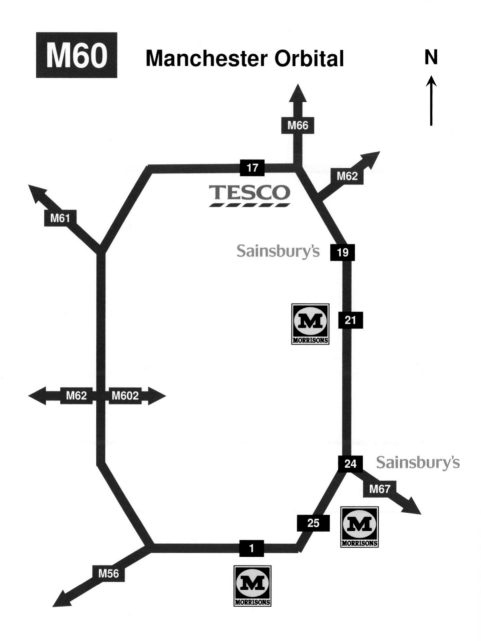

# Jct **1**     Stockport

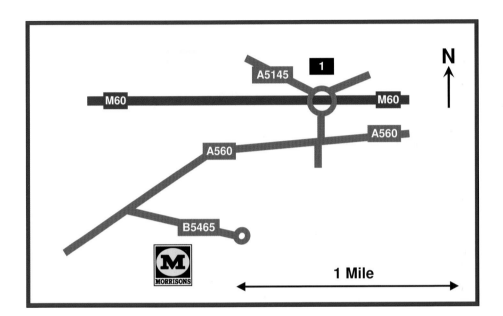

**MORRISONS**

Edgley Road
Cheadle Heath

**Opening Hours**

| | |
|---|---|
| *Mon - Fri* | 08:30 - 21:00 |
| *Sat* | 08:00 - 21:00 |
| *Sun* | 10:00 - 16:00 |

Tel: 0161 4777557

*Directions:*
Head south from motorway for 200 yards signposted Cheadle Heath. Turn right onto A560 signposted Cheadle Heath and head west for 3/4 mile. Turn left onto B5465. Store is 1/4 mile ahead on the right.

# Jct **17**     Prestwich

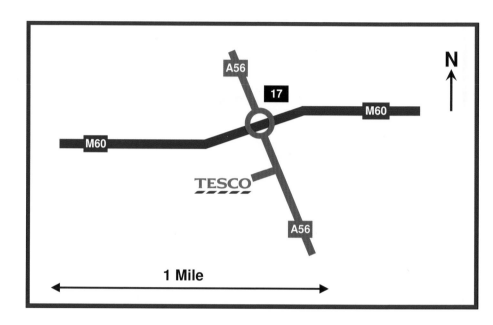

## TESCO

|  | | **Opening Hours** |
|---|---|---|
| Prestwich | **Mon - Fri** | 08:00 - 24 hr |
| Manchester | **Sat** | 24 hr - 21:00 |
|  | **Sun** | 10:00 - 16:00 |

Tel: 0161 910 9400

**Directions:**
Head south on A56 towards Prestwich and Manchester. Store is 1/4 mile ahead on the right in Valley Park Road.

# Jct **19**     Middleton

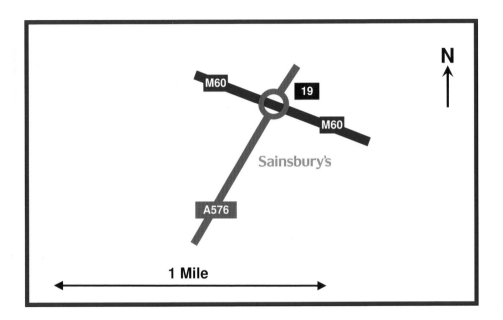

## Sainsbury's

170 Heaton Park Road West
Higher Brackley

**Opening Hours**
| | |
|---|---|
| **Mon - Fri** | 08:00 - 22:00 |
| **Sat** | 07:30 - 22:00 |
| **Sun** | 10:00 - 16:00 |

Tel: 0161 740 5738

**Directions:**
Head south on A576 towards Manchester. Store is 1/4 mile ahead on the left.

# Jct **21**     Chadderton

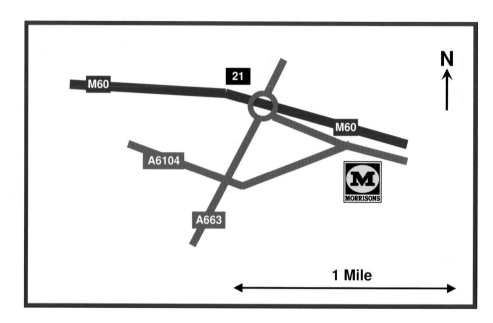

**MORRISONS**
Holinwood Avenue
Chadderton

Tel: 0161 6821114

| | *Opening Hours* | |
|---|---|---|
| *Mon - Fri* | 08:30 - 20:00 |
| *Sat* | 08:00 - 20:00 |
| *Sun* | 10:00 - 16:00 |

*Directions:*
Head east on A6104 towards Failsworth. Store is on the right after 1/2 mile.

# Jct **24**     Denton

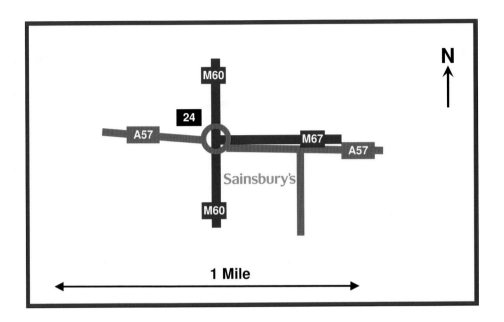

# Sainsbury's

Oldham Street
Denton
Manchester

Tel: 0161 335 0929

**Opening Hours**

| | |
|---|---|
| *Mon - Fri* | 08:00 - 22:00 |
| *Sat* | 07:00 - 22:00 |
| *Sun* | 10:00 - 16:00 |

***Directions:***
Head east along A57 towards Denton town centre. Take first right after 1/4 mile into Oldham street. Store is on the right.

# Jct **25**     **Bredbury**

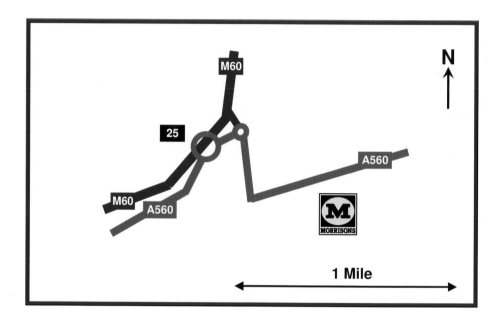

Stockport Road West
Stockport

**Opening Hours**

| | | |
|---|---|---|
| *Mon - Fri* | 08:30 - 20:00 |
| *Sat* | 08:00 - 20:00 |
| *Sun* | 11:00 - 17:00 |

Tel: 0161 4306997

*Directions:*
Head east from junction on A560 signposted Bredbury. Store is on the right after 3/4 mile.

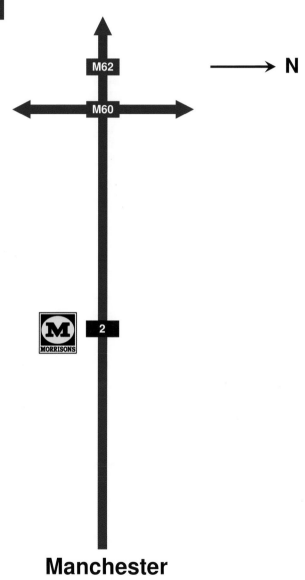

# Jct **2**    Eccles

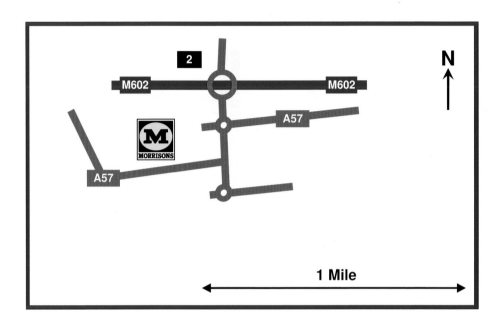

**1 Mile**

**MORRISONS**
7 Irwell Place
Eccles

***Opening Hours***
**Mon - Fri**  08:00 - 20:00
**Sat**  08:00 - 20:00
**Sun**  10:00 - 16:00

Tel: 0161 789 1229

***Directions:***
Head south from junction. Cross over first roundabout and then turn right along A57. Store is 1/4 mile ahead on the right.

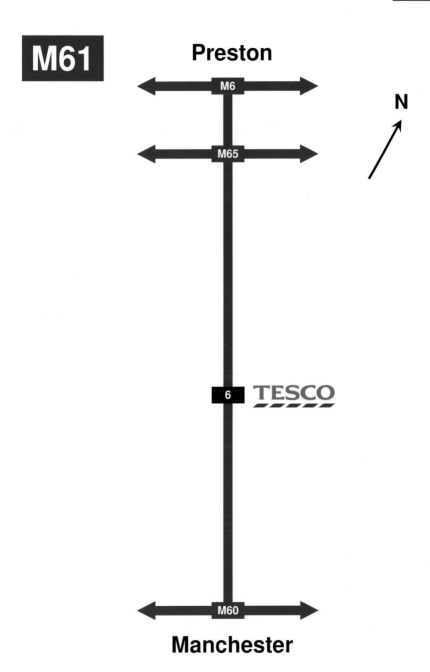

# Jct 6    Horwich

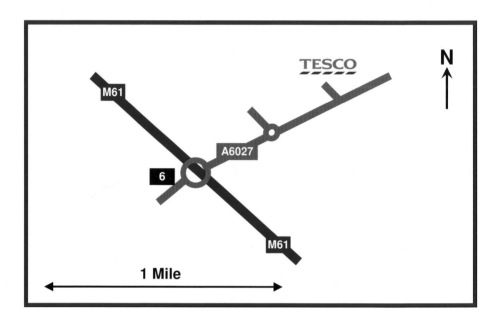

## TESCO

| | | **Opening Hours** |
|---|---|---|
| Mansell Way | **Mon - Fri** | 08:00 - 24 hr |
| Horwich | **Sat** | 24 hr - 21:00 |
| Bolton | **Sun** | 10:00 - 16:00 |

Tel: 01204 517600

**Directions:**
Head north on A6027 towards Bolton and Horwich. Store is 1 mile ahead on the left in Mansell Way.

**M62**

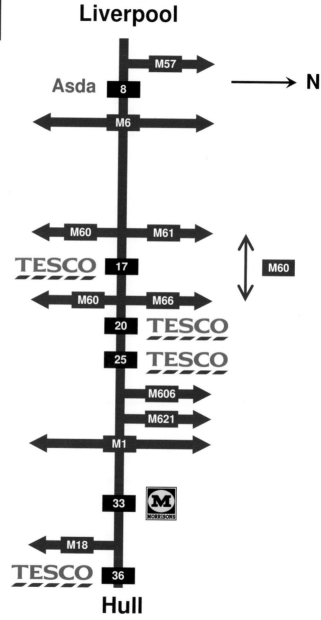

**Liverpool**

M57

Asda — 8

M6

M60 — M61

TESCO — 17

M60

M60 — M66

20 — TESCO

25 — TESCO

M606

M621

M1

33 — MORRISONS

M18 — 33

TESCO — 36

**Hull**

N

107

# Jct **8**     Warrington

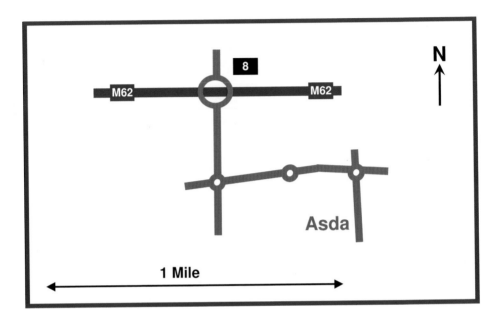

# Asda

Westbrook Shopping Centre
Cromwell Avenue
Warrington

Tel: 01925 638633

*Opening Hours*

| | |
|---|---|
| **Mon - Fri** | 08:30 - 24hr |
| **Sat** | 24hr - 22:00 |
| **Sun** | 10:30 - 16:30 |

*Directions:*
Head south from motorway for 1/2 mile towards Westbrook. Turn left at first roundabout. Proceed straight across the next roundabout. Turn right at the third roundabout, store is on the right in the Westbrook shopping centre.

# Jct **17**    Prestwich

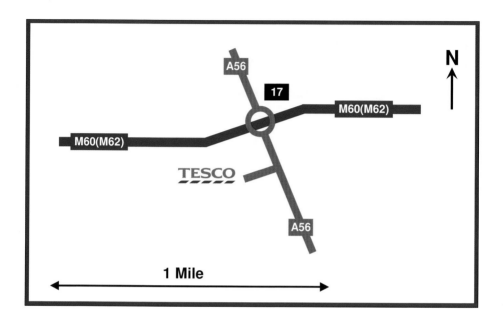

# TESCO

Prestwich
Manchester

**Opening Hours**

| | | |
|---|---|---|
| **Mon - Fri** | 08:00 - 24 hr |
| **Sat** | 24 hr - 21:00 |
| **Sun** | 10:00 - 16:00 |

Tel: 0161 910 9400

**Directions:**
Head south on A56 towards Prestwich and Manchester. Store is 1/4 mile ahead on the right in Valley Park Road.

# Jct **20**     **Rochdale**

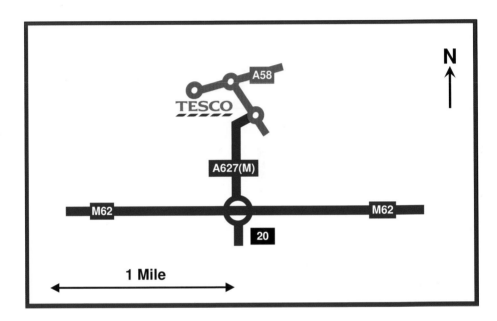

# TESCO

Silk Street
Rochdale

**Opening Hours**

| | |
|---|---|
| **Mon - Fri** | 08:00 - 24 hr |
| **Sat** | 24 hr - 21:00 |
| **Sun** | 10:00 - 16:00 |

Tel: 01706 706600

**Directions:**
Head north on A627(M) towards Rochdale. Turn left on A664 and then left
again on A58 towards Bury. Turn left at next roundabout into Silk Street.
Store is immediately on the left.

# Jct 25   Brighouse

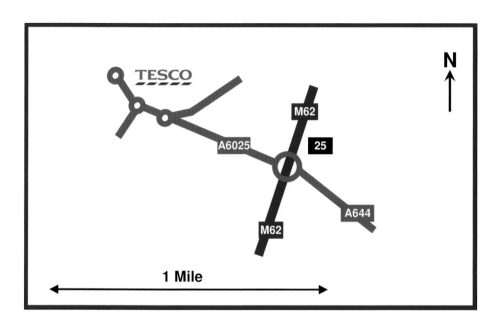

## TESCO

Huddersfield Road
Brighouse

Tel: 01484 227500

**Opening Hours**

| | |
|---|---|
| *Mon - Fri* | 08:00 - 24 hr |
| *Sat* | 24 hr - 21:00 |
| *Sun* | 10:00 - 16:00 |

**Directions:**
Head west on A6025 towards Brighouse for 1 mile. Turn right at second roundabout. Store is on the right.

# Jct **33**    **Knottingley**

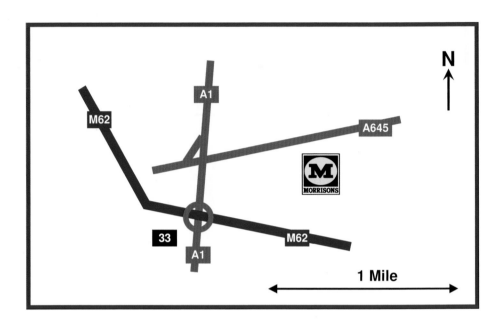

N

M62

A1

A645

M62

33

A1

1 Mile

**MORRISONS**

Marine Villa Road
Knottingley

Tel: 01977 679401

***Opening Hours***

| | |
|---|---|
| ***Mon - Fri*** | 08:00 - 20:00 |
| ***Sat*** | 08:00 - 20:00 |
| ***Sun*** | 10:00 - 16:00 |

***Directions:***
Head north on A1 for 1/2 mile. Turn left following signs A645 towards
Knottingley and cross the A1. Store is 3/4 mile ahead on the right.

# Jct 36　　Goole

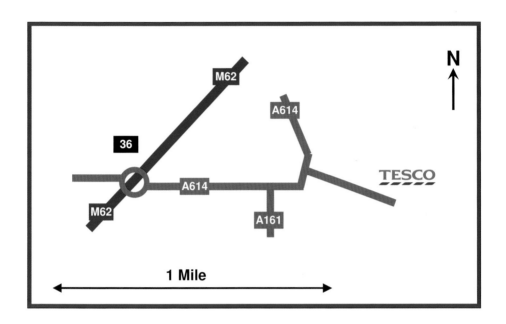

## TESCO

| | **Opening Hours** | |
|---|---|---|
| Boothferry Road | **Mon - Fri** | 08:00 - 24 hr |
| Goole | **Sat** | 24 hr - 21:00 |
| Lincolnshire | **Sun** | 10:00 - 16:00 |

Tel: 01405 665400

**Directions:**
Head east on A614 towards Goole. Continue towards Howden then after 3/4 mile, turn right into Boothferry Road. Store is 1/2 mile ahead on the left.

M65

Preston

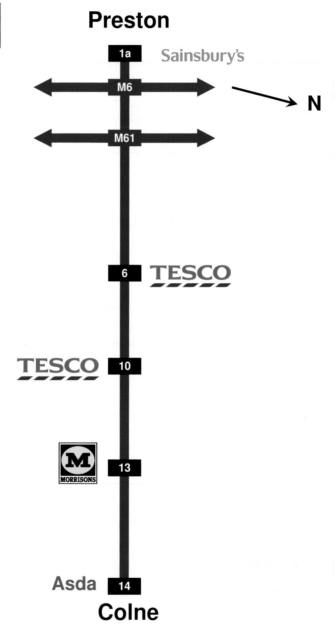

1a  Sainsbury's

M6

N

M61

6  TESCO

TESCO  10

M
MORRISONS  13

Asda  14

Colne

# Jct **1a**    **Bamber Bridge**

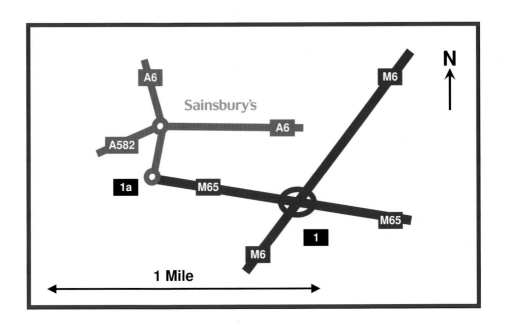

## Sainsbury's

Cuerden Way
Bamber Bridge
Preston

Tel: 01772 627762

**Opening Hours**

| | |
|---|---|
| *Mon - Fri* | 08:00 - 22:00 |
| *Sat* | 07:00 - 22:00 |
| *Sun* | 10:00 - 16:00 |

**Directions:**
Proceed to the end of the motorway (jct 1a) and head north on A6 towards Bamber Bridge. Turn right at the first roundabout. Store is on the left.

# Jct **6**      **Blackburn**

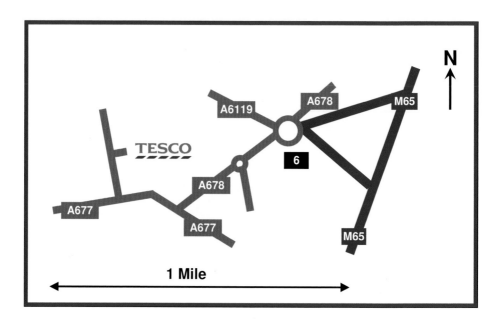

# Jct 10     Burnley

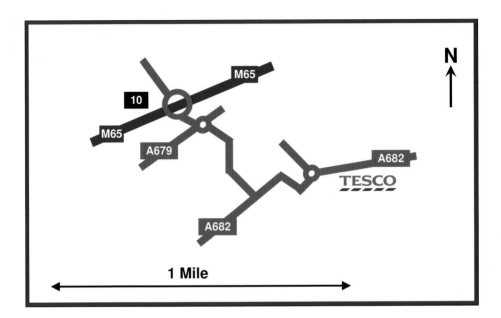

## TESCO

Centenary Way
Finsley Gate
Burnley

Tel: 01282 667400

**Opening Hours**

| | |
|---|---|
| **Mon - Fri** | 08:00 - 24 hr |
| **Sat** | 24 hr - 21:00 |
| **Sun** | 10:00 - 16:00 |

**Directions:**
Head south from the motorway towards Burnley town centre. Go straight across the first roundabout and follow this road to the end. At the end turn left. Continue over the next roundabout and the store is on the right.

# Jct 13     Nelson

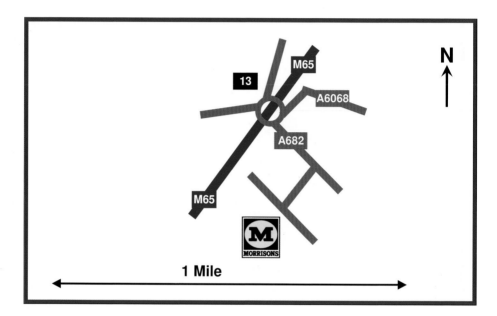

Pendle Street
Nelson

**Tel: 01282 449196**

**Opening Hours**

| | |
|---|---|
| **Mon - Fri** | 08:00 - 20:00 |
| **Sat** | 08:00 - 20:00 |
| **Sun** | 10:00 - 16:00 |

**Directions:**
Head south towards Nelson town centre on the A682. After ¼ mile take the first right into Clayton Street. Store is 1/4 mile ahead.

# Jct **14**　　　**Colne**

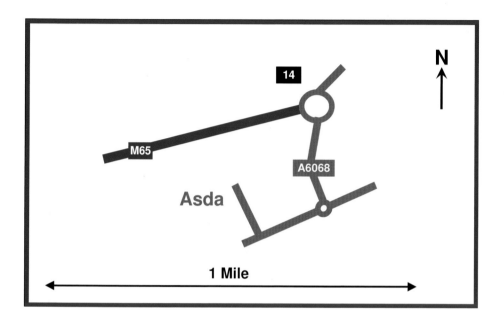

# Asda

Corporation Street
Colne

**Opening Hours**

| | |
|---|---|
| **Mon - Fri** | 08:00 - 24hr |
| **Sat** | 24hr - 22:00 |
| **Sun** | 10:00 - 16:00 |

Tel: 01282 870156

**Directions:**
Head south on A6068 towards Nelson. Turn right at the roundabout. Take the third road on the right Corporation street. Store is 1/4 mile ahead.

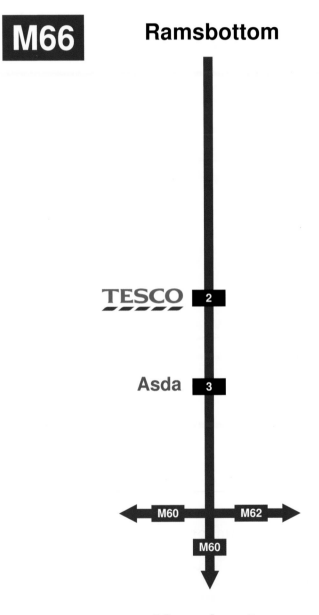

M66

Ramsbottom

N

TESCO 2

Asda 3

◄ M60          M62 ►

M60

Manchester

# Jct **2**     **Bury**

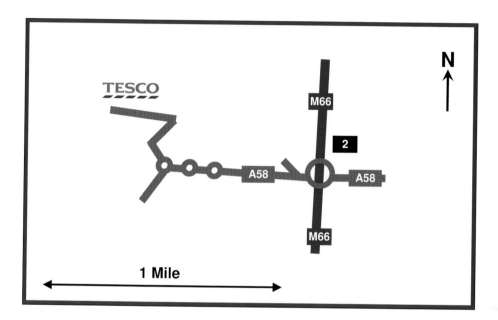

## TESCO

Woodfield Retail Park
Peel Way
Bury

Tel: 0161 912 9500

**Opening Hours**
| | |
|---|---|
| **Mon - Fri** | 08:00 - 24 hr |
| **Sat** | 24 hr - 21:00 |
| **Sun** | 10:00 - 16:00 |

**Directions:**
Head west on A58 for 2/3 mile towards Bury. Turn right at third roundabout onto ring road. Continue on ring road until store is on the right in Woodfield Retail Park.

# Jct **3**     **Bury**

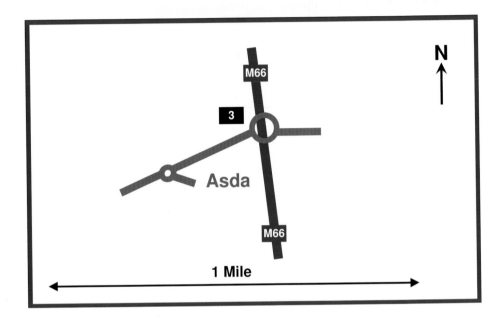

# Asda

Pilsworth Industrial Estate
Pilsworth Road
Bury

Tel: 0161 766 9735

**Opening Hours**

| | |
|---|---|
| *Mon - Fri* | 08:30 - 24hr |
| *Sat* | 24hr - 22:00 |
| *Sun* | 10:30 - 16:30 |

*Directions:*
Head west from junction towards Whitefield and take first left into Pilsworth Industrial estate. Store is ahead on the left.

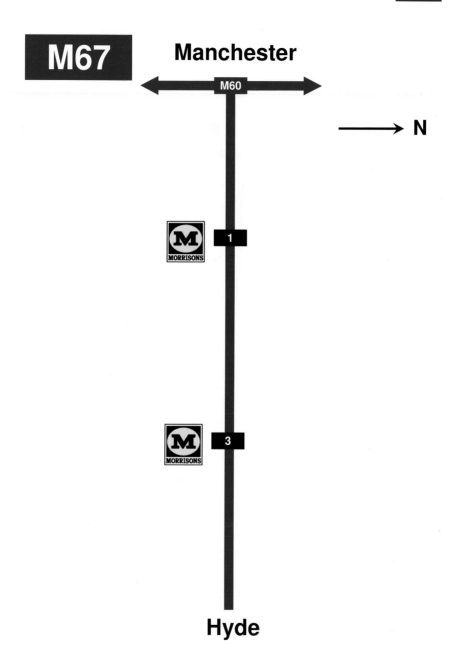

# Jct **1**   Denton

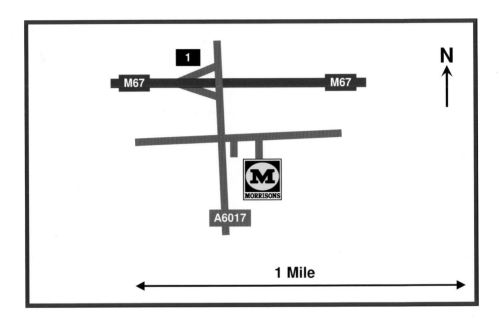

**MORRISONS**

Saxon Street
Denton

Tel: 0161 337 8613

| | **Opening Hours** | |
|---|---|---|
| *Mon - Fri* | 08:30 - 20:00 | |
| *Sat* | 08:00 - 20:00 | |
| *Sun* | 10:00 - 16:00 | |

*Directions:*
**Only accessible when heading eastbound!**
Head south on A617 towards Denton town centre. Turn left at crossroads signposted Hyde. Take the second right and store is on the right.

**M67**

# Jct **3**      Hyde

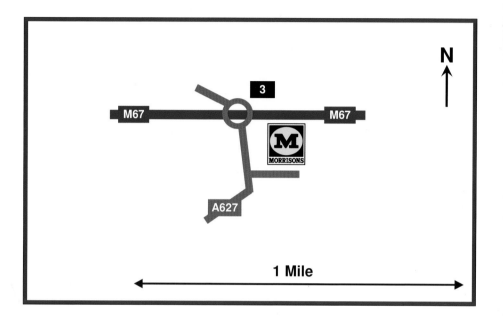

|  | **Opening Hours** |  |
|---|---|---|
| Mottram Road | **Mon - Fri** | 08:30 - 20:00 |
| Hyde | **Sat** | 08:00 - 20:00 |
|  | **Sun** | 10:00 - 16:00 |

Tel: 0161 3687122

**Directions:**
Head south on A627 towards Hyde town centre. Take first left and store is immediately on the left by the junction.